OF COMPOSERS

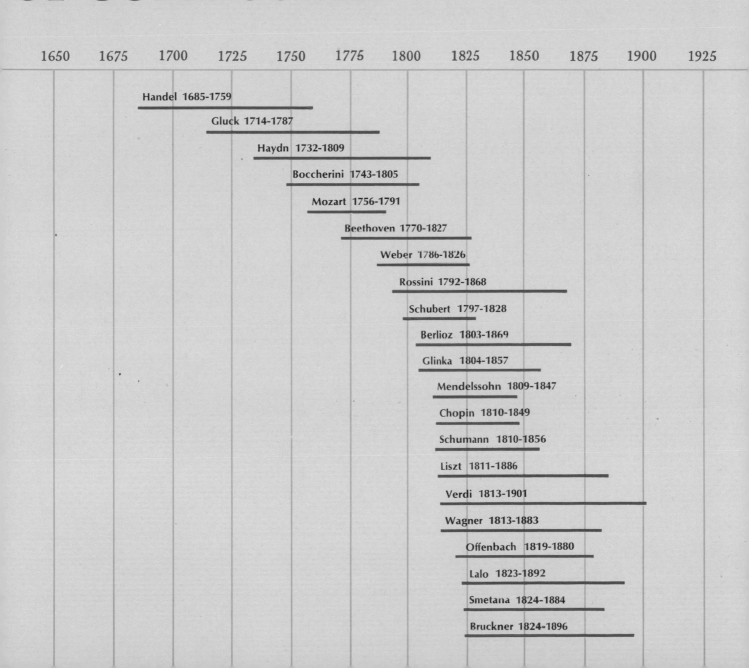

1650	1675	1700	1725	1750	1775	1800	1825	1850	1875	1900	1925

Handel 1685-1759

Gluck 1714-1787

Haydn 1732-1809

Boccherini 1743-1805

Mozart 1756-1791

Beethoven 1770-1827

Weber 1786-1826

Rossini 1792-1868

Schubert 1797-1828

Berlioz 1803-1869

Glinka 1804-1857

Mendelssohn 1809-1847

Chopin 1810-1849

Schumann 1810-1856

Liszt 1811-1886

Verdi 1813-1901

Wagner 1813-1883

Offenbach 1819-1880

Lalo 1823-1892

Smetana 1824-1884

Bruckner 1824-1896

THE STORY OF GREAT MUSIC

AN INDEX
TO THE
RECORDINGS

TIME-LIFE RECORDS   NEW YORK

EDITOR: Jay Gold
ASSISTANT EDITORS: David Johnson, Jeanne LeMonnier, Joan S. Reiter MUSIC ASSISTANT: Karl F. Reuling
RESEARCHERS: Helen Harman, Michele Wood EDITORIAL CONSULTANT: Jacques Barzun

MANAGING DIRECTOR: Francis M. Scott III
ASSISTANT TO THE MANAGING DIRECTOR: J. Wendell Forbes
BUSINESS MANAGER: Peter L. Hoyt PROMOTION MANAGER: William C. Kiefer
INTERNATIONAL MARKETING MANAGERS: Gary C. Burger, Charles C. Colt, Jr.

"The Story of Great Music" is produced by TIME-LIFE RECORDS in cooperation with Angel Records, a
subsidiary of Capitol Records, Inc., Robert E. Myers, Angel Repertoire Director.

Editors' Note

This index covers the recordings included in the TIME-LIFE RECORDS series *The Story of Great Music* and its supplementary volumes, *Concerts of Great Music*.

Each volume of *The Story of Great Music* is represented by an abbreviation listed below. The same abbreviations, followed by the word "Concerts," are used to indicate the volumes of *Concerts of Great Music*.

From the Renaissance: Renaissance
The Baroque Era: Baroque
Age of Elegance: Elegance
Age of Revolution: Revolution
The Romantic Era: Romantic
The Opulent Era: Opulent
Prelude to Modern Music: Prelude
The Early Twentieth Century: Twentieth
The Music of Today: Today
The Spanish Style: Spanish
Slavic Traditions: Slavic

The works are listed alphabetically according to title, composer, music forms (Operas, Sonatas) and compositions for specific instruments such as Harpsichord, Violin. Unless otherwise indicated, the works are presented in their entirety.

Full listings of each volume may be found under the appropriate title. The illustrations appearing on the pages with these listings are "ghost" drawings made from the works of art on the slipcase covers of the individual volumes.

A

Abdelazer, Music for, Purcell, BAROQUE side 1 band 5

Abduction from the Seraglio, The: Selections, Mozart, ELEGANCE CONCERTS side 4 band 2, side 5

"Absence," Berlioz, ROMANTIC CONCERTS side 4 band 3

Academic Festival Overture, Op. 80, Brahms, OPULENT side 5 band 3

"Ach Herr, mich armen Sünder," Buxtehude, RENAISSANCE CONCERTS side 7 band 4

"Adieu, sweet Amaryllis," Wilbye, RENAISSANCE side 2 band 8

"Ah, el novio no quiere dinero," Anon., SPANISH CONCERTS side 3 band 1

"Albaicín, El," Albéniz, SPANISH side 2 band 3

ALBENIZ, Isaac:
Iberia, Selections: "Evocación," "Triana," "El Albaicín," SPANISH side 2 band 1
"Preludio," SPANISH CONCERTS side 2 band 2
"Serenata Española," Op. 181, SPANISH CONCERTS side 2 band 3
"Sevilla," SPANISH CONCERTS side 2 band 1

Alborada del Gracioso, Ravel, SPANISH CONCERTS side 9 band 1

Alegria del Batallon, La: "Canción de la Gitana," Serrano, SPANISH CONCERTS side 8 band 3.

Alexander Nevsky: Cantata, Op. 78, Prokofiev, TWENTIETH CONCERTS side 8, side 9 band 1

ALFONSO EL SABIO, *Cantigas de Santa Maria:* "Rosa das rosas," "Maravillosos e piadosos," SPANISH CONCERTS side 3 band 2

"Allemainge," Susato, RENAISSANCE side 5 band 1

"Almaine," Anon., RENAISSANCE side 2 band 2

Amadigi: Selections, Handel, BAROQUE CONCERTS side 6 band 1

Amants magnifiques, Les: Suite, Lully, RENAISSANCE side 3 band 3

American in Paris, An, Gershwin, TWENTIETH side 7 band 1

American Quartet (String Quartet No. 12 in F Major, Op. 96), Dvořák, SLAVIC CONCERTS side 8

Amor Brujo, El, Falla, SPANISH CONCERTS side 10

Amphitryon, Music for, Purcell, BAROQUE side 1 band 5

Andalusian Songs, Ancient. *See* THE SPANISH STYLE CONCERTS side 3 band 1

Années de Pèlerinage: Selections, Liszt, ROMANTIC CONCERTS side 7

Appalachian Spring: Suite, Copland, TO-DAY side 5

Apothéose de Corelli, L', Couperin, BA-ROQUE CONCERTS side 7 band 2

ARAUJO, Juan de, "Los Negritos," SPAN-ISH side 7 band 2

Archduke Trio (Trio in B Flat Major, Op. 97), Beethoven, REVOLUTION CON-CERTS side 7 band 4, side 8

Arlequine, L', Couperin, BAROQUE side 6 band 1

"Au Cimetière," Berlioz, ROMANTIC CONCERTS side 4 band 4

"Aus der Tiefe" *(Psalm 130),* Schütz, RENAISSANCE CONCERTS side 7 band 1

"Ave Maria," Victoria, SPANISH side 7 band 1

"Ave verum Corpus," Byrd, RENAIS-SANCE side 6 band 5

"Ave verum Corpus," K. 618, Mozart, ELEGANCE CONCERTS side 2 band 5

"Ay triste que vengo," Encina, SPAN-ISH side 3 band 1

B

BABBITT, Milton, Ensembles for Synthe-sizer, Part 1, TODAY side 6 band 1

BACH, Johann Sebastian:

Brandenburg Concerto No. 2 in F Major, BWV. 1047, BAROQUE side 7 band 2

Cantata BWV. 140, *Wachet auf (Sleep-ers Awake),* BAROQUE CONCERTS side 2 band 3, side 3

Vivaldi-Bach, Concerto in A Minor for Four Harpsichords and Strings, BWV. 1065, BAROQUE side 2 band 2

Concerto in D Minor for Two Violins and Strings, BWV. 1043, BAROQUE CONCERTS side 5 band 1

St. Matthew Passion: Selections, BA-ROQUE side 4

Toccata and Fugue in D Minor for Organ, BWV. 565, BAROQUE side 6 band 3

Trio Sonata No. 5 in C Major for Or-gan, BWV. 529, BAROQUE CON-CERTS side 9 band 1

Bachianas Brasileiras No. 1, Villa-Lobos, TWENTIETH CONCERTS side 3 band 1

Bachianas Brasileiras No. 5, Villa-Lobos, TWENTIETH side 7 band 2

BALAKIREV, Mili, *Islamey* ("Oriental Fantasy"), SLAVIC side 1 band 4

Ballade No. 1 in G Minor, Op. 23, Chopin, ROMANTIC side 2 band 3

Ballet de la Nuit: Selections, Lully, RE-NAISSANCE CONCERTS side 8 band 3

Ballet d'Hercule: Selections, Lully, RENAISSANCE CONCERTS side 8 band 2

BALLET MUSIC:

    Amants magnifiques, Les: Suite, Lully, RENAISSANCE side 3 band 3

    Amor Brujo, El, Falla, SPANISH CONCERTS side 10

    Appalachian Spring, Copland, TODAY side 5

    Ballet de la Nuit: Selections, Lully, RENAISSANCE CONCERTS side 8 band 3

    Ballet d'Hercule: Selections, Lully, RENAISSANCE CONCERTS side 8 band 2

    Ballo delle Ingrate, Il: Ballet Music, Monteverdi, RENAISSANCE side 5 band 6

    Création du monde, La, Milhaud, TWENTIETH side 6 band 3

    Daphnis et Chloé: Suite No. 2, Ravel, PRELUDE side 8 band 2

    Facsimile, Bernstein, TODAY CONCERTS side 4 band 3

    Fancy Free: Excerpts, Bernstein, TODAY side 6 band 2

    Pulcinella: Suite, Stravinsky, TWENTIETH CONCERTS side 1

    Rodeo: Four Dance Episodes, Copland, TODAY CONCERTS side 3 band 2, side 4 band 1

    Sacre du Printemps, Le, Stravinsky, TWENTIETH side 2 band 2, side 3 band 1

    Swan Lake: Suite, Tchaikovsky, OPULENT side 6

    Three-Cornered Hat, The, Falla, SPANISH side 7 band 3, side 8

    William Tell: Ballet Music, Rossini, REVOLUTION CONCERTS side 5 band 2

Ballo delle Ingrate, Il: Ballet Music, Monteverdi, RENAISSANCE side 5 band 6

Ballo in Maschera, Un: Selections, Verdi, ROMANTIC side 3 band 3

Barberillo de Lavapiés, El: "Canción de Paloma," Barbieri, SPANISH CONCERTS side 8 band 7

Barber of Seville, The: Selections, Rossini, REVOLUTION side 5

BARBIERI, Francisco, *El Barberillo de Lavapiés:* "Canción de Paloma," SPANISH CONCERTS side 8 band 7

BAROQUE ERA, THE

    Side 1, Purcell, Theater Music and Songs

        Band 1, Music from *The Fairy Queen*

        Band 2, Music from *The Indian Queen*

        Band 3, Two Duets: "Let Us Wander," "Lost Is My Quiet"

        Band 4, Music from *King Arthur*

        Band 5, Music for Dramatic Works:

BAROQUE ERA, THE: *Continued*
  Abdelazer, Distressed Inno-
  cence, Amphitryon, The Double
  Dealer
Side 2
  Band 1, Telemann, Concerto in B
  Flat Major for Three Oboes,
  Three Violins and Basso Con-
  tinuo
  Band 2, Vivaldi-Bach, Concerto in
  A Minor for Four Harpsichords
  and Strings, BWV. 1065
Side 3
  Band 1, Corelli, *Concerto Grosso*
  in G Minor, Op. 6 No. 8 ("Christ-
  mas Concerto")
  Band 2, Vivaldi, Concerto in D
  Major, Op. 10 No. 3 ("Il Gar-
  dellino")
Side 4, Bach, *St. Matthew Passion*
  Band 1, Chorus: "Kommt, ihr
  Töchter"
  Band 2, Recitative: "Petrus aber
  sass draussen im Palast," Cho-
  rus: "Wahrlich, du bist auch
  einer von denen," Recitative:
  "Da hub er an, sich zu ver-
  fluchen," Aria: "Erbarme dich,
  mein Gott"
  Band 3, Chorale: "O Haupt voll
  Blut und Wunden"

Side 5, Handel, *Messiah*
  Band 1, Recitative: "Comfort ye,"
  Air: "Ev'ry valley"
  Band 2, Chorus: "For unto us a
  Child is born"
  Band 3, Air: "He shall feed His
  flock"
  Band 4, Chorus: "Behold the Lamb
  of God"
  Band 5, Chorus: "Hallelujah!"
Side 6
  Band 1, Couperin, *Les Barricades*
  Mystérieuses, L'Arlequine
  Band 2, Rameau, *Gavotte Variée*
  Band 3, Bach, Toccata and Fugue
  in D Minor, BWV. 565
Side 7
  Band 1, Scarlatti, Sonatas for harp-
  sichord: in A minor, L. 429; in D
  Major, L. 164
  Band 2, Bach, Brandenburg Con-
  certo No. 2 in F Major, BWV.
  1047
Side 8, Handel, *The Water Music*
  Band 1, Suite in G Major
  Band 2, Suite in D Major
BAROQUE ERA, THE (CONCERTS)
  Side 1, Telemann, Suite in C Major
  ("Water Music")
Side 2
  Bands 1-2, Handel, Concerto in B

Flat Major for Harp and Orchestra

Band 3, Bach, Cantata BWV. 140, *Wachet auf, ruft uns die Stimme (Sleepers Awake):* Beginning, Chorus: "Wachet auf, ruft uns die Stimme"

Side 3, Bach, Cantata BWV. 140, *Wachet auf, ruft uns die Stimme (Sleepers Awake):* Conclusion

Band 1, Recitative: "Er kommt, er kommt"

Band 2, Duet: "Wann kommst du, mein Heil?"

Band 3, Chorale: "Zion hört die Wächter singen"

Band 4, Recitative: "So geh' herein zu mir"

Band 5, Duet: "Mein Freund ist mein!"

Band 6, Chorale: "Gloria sei dir gesungen"

Side 4

Band 1, Scarlatti, Sonata in B Flat Major, L. 498 (K. 202)

Band 2, Scarlatti, Sonata in D Major, L. 461 (K. 29)

Band 3, Scarlatti, Sonata in B Major, L. 450 (K. 245)

Band 4, Couperin, *Concert Royal* No. 2 in D Major

Side 5

Bands 1-3, Bach, Concerto in D Minor for Two Violins and Strings, BWV. 1043

Band 4, Vivaldi, Concerto in A Major for Two Orchestras

Side 6, Selections from Baroque Opera

Band 1, Handel, *Amadigi,* Act 3: Sinfonia

Band 2, Handel, *Amadigi,* Act 2: "D'un sventurato amante," "Pena tiranna io sento al core"

Band 3, Handel, *Amadigi,* Act 2: "Mi deride l'amante," "Desterò dall' empia dite"

Band 4, Rameau, *Les Indes galantes,* Second Entrée: "Invocation and Hymn to the Sun"

Band 5, Purcell, *Dido and Aeneas,* Act 3: Closing Scene

Side 7

Band 1, Corelli, *Concerto Grosso* in F Major, Op. 6 No. 9

Bands 2-5, Couperin, *Le Parnasse ou L'Apothéose de Corelli*

Side 8

Band 1, Purcell, Trio Sonata in G Major, Z. 797

Band 2, Purcell, Fantasia in F Major, Z. 745 ("Upon One Note")

BAROQUE ERA, THE (CONCERTS):
Continued
    Band 3, Handel, *Concerto Grosso*
    in D Major, Op. 6 No. 5
  Side 9
    Bands 1-3, Bach, Trio Sonata No.
    5 in C Major for Organ, BWV.
    529
    Band 4, Vivaldi, *Gloria:* "Gloria in
    excelsis Deo"
    Band 5, Vivaldi, *Gloria:* "Et in terra
    pax"
  Side 10, Vivaldi, *Gloria:* Conclusion
    Band 1, "Laudamus te"
    Band 2, "Gratias agimus tibi,"
    "Propter magnam gloriam"
    Band 3, "Domine Deus, Rex cael-
    estis"
    Band 4, "Domini Fili unigenite"
    Band 5, "Domini Deus, Agnus Dei"
    Band 6, "Qui tollis peccata mundi"
    Band 7, "Qui sedes ad dexteram
    Patris"
    Band 8, "Quoniam tu solus Sanc-
    tus"
    Band 9, "Cum Sancto Spiritu"
Baroque Opera, Selections from. *See*
THE BAROQUE ERA CONCERTS,
side 6
Barricades Mystérieuses, Les, Couperin,
BAROQUE side 6 band 1

Bartered Bride, The: Act 3, Smetana,
SLAVIC CONCERTS side 9, side 10
Bartered Bride, The: Overture, Smetana,
SLAVIC side 7 band 1
BARTOK, Béla:
  Concerto for Orchestra, TWENTIETH
  side 3 band 2, side 4
  Concerto No. 3 for Piano and Or-
  chestra, TWENTIETH CONCERTS
  side 2
  Music for String Instruments, Percus-
  sion and Celesta, TWENTIETH
  CONCERTS side 7
BEETHOVEN, Ludwig van:
  Concerto No. 4 in G Major, Op. 58
  for piano, REVOLUTION side 3
  band 2, side 4 band 1
  Consecration of the House: Overture,
  Op. 124, REVOLUTION CON-
  CERTS side 1 band 1
  Leonore Overture No. 3, Op. 72,
  REVOLUTION side 1 band 1
  Quartet No. 16 in F Major, Op. 135
  for strings, REVOLUTION side 6
  Sonata No. 5 in F Major, Op. 24
  ("Spring") for violin and piano,
  ELEGANCE CONCERTS side 3
  Sonata No. 27 in E Minor, Op. 90 for
  piano, REVOLUTION side 4 band 2
  Symphony No. 1 in C Major, Op. 21,
  ELEGANCE side 7

Symphony No. 3 in E Flat Major, Op. 55 ("Eroica"), REVOLUTION side 7, side 8

Symphony No. 4 in B Flat Major, Op. 60, REVOLUTION CONCERTS side 1 band 2, side 2

Trio in B Flat Major, Op. 97 ("Archduke"), REVOLUTION CONCERTS side 7 band 4, side 8

Belshazzar's Feast, Walton, TODAY CONCERTS side 1 band 4, side 2

"Benedictus Dominus," Andrea Gabrieli, RENAISSANCE CONCERTS side 3 band 1

BERG, Alban:

Four Pieces for Clarinet and Piano, Op. 5, TWENTIETH side 2 band 1

Lulu: Excerpts, TWENTIETH CONCERTS side 4 band 2

BERNSTEIN, Leonard:

Facsimile (A Choreographic Essay), TODAY CONCERTS side 4 band 3

Fancy Free: Excerpts, TODAY side 6 band 2

Bergamasca, La, Frescobaldi, RENAISSANCE side 5 band 3

BERLIOZ, Hector:

La Damnation de Faust, Op. 24: Part 1, ROMANTIC CONCERTS side 6 band 1

Les Nuits d'été, Op. 7, ROMANTIC CONCERTS side 3 band 5, side 4

Symphonie fantastique, ROMANTIC side 7, side 8

Les Troyens: "Royal Hunt and Storm," ROMANTIC CONCERTS side 6 band 2

BIZET, Georges, *Carmen:* Act 4, SPANISH side 4 band 2

BOCCHERINI, Luigi:

Overture in D Major, Op. 43, ELEGANCE side 1 band 1

Symphony in C Minor, ELEGANCE CONCERTS side 7 band 3

Bohème, La: Act 3, Puccini, PRELUDE side 6

Boris Godounov : Scenes, Moussorgsky, SLAVIC side 3, side 4

BORODIN, Alexander:

In the Steppes of Central Asia, SLAVIC side 1 band 3

Prince Igor: Polovtsian Dances, SLAVIC CONCERTS side 6 band 1

Symphony No. 2 in B Minor, SLAVIC CONCERTS side 6 band 2, side 7 band 1

BOULEZ, Pierre, *Le Soleil des Eaux:* Cantata, TODAY side 4 band 1

BRAHMS, Johannes:

Academic Festival Overture, Op. 80, OPULENT side 5 band 3

Sextet No. 1 in B Flat Major, Op. 18

for strings, OPULENT CONCERTS side 2, side 3 band 1

Symphony No. 2 in D Major, Op. 73, OPULENT side 1 band 2, side 2

Three Intermezzi, Op. 117, OPULENT CONCERTS side 3 band 2

Brandenburg Concerto No. 2 in F Major, BWV. 1047, Bach, BAROQUE side 7 band 2

"Bransle," Anon., RENAISSANCE CONCERTS side 6 band 1

BRITTEN, Benjamin:

"Four Sea Interludes," Op. 33A, from *Peter Grimes*, TODAY side 4 band 2

Variations on a Theme of Frank Bridge, Op. 10, TODAY CONCERTS side 6

BRUCKNER, Anton:

Mass No. 3 in F Minor ("The Great Mass"): Credo, Sanctus, Benedictus, OPULENT CONCERTS side 8

Symphony No. 4 in E Flat Major ("Romantic"), OPULENT side 7, side 8

"Buccinate in neomenia," Giovanni Gabrieli, RENAISSANCE side 1 band 1

BULL, John, "St. Thomas, Wake," RENAISSANCE CONCERTS side 6 band 4

BUXTEHUDE, Dietrich:

"Ach Herr, mich armen Sünder," RENAISSANCE CONCERTS side 7 band 4

"Laudate, pueri," RENAISSANCE side 3 band 2

"Mein Herz ist bereit," RENAISSANCE CONCERTS side 7 band 5

Prelude and Fugue in G Minor, RENAISSANCE side 3 band 1

BYRD, William:

"Ave verum Corpus," RENAISSANCE side 6 band 5

"A Gigg," RENAISSANCE side 2 band 4

"Haec dies," RENAISSANCE side 6 band 4

"Hey ho, to the greenwood," RENAISSANCE CONCERTS side 6 band 8

"Lamentationes" *(The Lamentations of Jeremiah the Prophet)*, RENAISSANCE CONCERTS side 1 band 3

"O quam gloriosum," RENAISSANCE side 6 band 6

"This Sweet and Merry Month," RENAISSANCE side 2 band 5

C

CABALLERO, Manuel Fernandez, *Gigantes y Cabezudas:* "Romanza de Pilar," SPANISH CONCERTS side 8 band 6

CAMPION, Thomas:
   "Oft have I sighed," RENAISSANCE side 2 band 3
   "Shall I come sweet love to thee," RENAISSANCE CONCERTS side 6 band 2
"Canción de la Gitana," Serrano, SPANISH CONCERTS side 8 band 3
"Canción de Paloma," Barbieri, SPANISH CONCERTS side 8 band 7
CANTATAS & ORATORIOS:
   Araujo, "Los Negritos," SPANISH side 7 band 2
   Bach, Cantata BWV. 140, *Wachet auf (Sleepers Awake)*, BAROQUE CONCERTS side 2 band 3, side 3
   Boulez, *Le Soleil des Eaux*, TODAY side 4 band 1
   Buxtehude, "Mein Herz ist bereit," RENAISSANCE CONCERTS side 7 band 5
   Handel, *Messiah:* Selections, BAROQUE side 5
   Haydn, *The Creation:* Part 1, ELEGANCE side 3 band 2, side 4
   Prokofiev, *Alexander Nevsky* Cantata, Op. 78, TWENTIETH CONCERTS side 8, side 9, band 1
   Schütz, *Christmas Oratorio*, SWV. 435A: Excerpts, RENAISSANCE side 7
   Schütz, "Herr, nun lässest du deinen Diener," RENAISSANCE CONCERTS side 7 band 3
   Shostakovich, *The Execution of Stepan Razin*, Op. 119, TODAY side 7
   Vaughan Williams, *Hodie*, TODAY CONCERTS side 9, side 10
   Walton, *Belshazzar's Feast*, TODAY CONCERTS side 1 band 4, side 2
Cantigas de Santa Maria: "Rosa das rosas," "Maravillosos e piadosos," Alfonso El Sabio, SPANISH CONCERTS side 3 band 2
Canzona, Giovanni Gabrieli, RENAISSANCE side 1 band 2
"Capriccio del soggetto *Fra Jacopin* scritto sopra l'aria di *Ruggiero*," Frescobaldi, RENAISSANCE CONCERTS side 2 band 3
Capriccio Espagnol, Op. 34, Rimsky-Korsakov, SPANISH CONCERTS side 1 band 2
"Carceleras," Chapí, SPANISH side 6 band 1
Carmen: Act 4, Bizet, SPANISH side 4 band 2
"Cathédrale engloutie, La," Debussy, PRELUDE side 7 band 3
CHABRIER, Emmanuel, *España*, SPANISH side 4 band 1
CHAPI, Ruperto, *Las Hijas del Zebedeo:* "Carceleras," SPANISH side 6 band 1
CHARPENTIER, Marc-Antoine:

"Marche de triomphe," RENAIS-SANCE CONCERTS side 8 band 1

"Second Air de Trompettes," RENAIS-SANCE CONCERTS side 8 band 4

"Chiome d'oro," Monteverdi, RENAIS-SANCE CONCERTS side 2 band 2

CHOPIN, Frédéric:

Compositions for Piano: Mazurka No. 17 in B Flat Minor, Op. 24 No. 4; Polonaise No. 3 in A Major, Op. 40 No. 1; Ballade No. 1 in G Minor, Op. 23; Waltz No. 6 in D Flat Major, Op. 64 No. 1; Waltz No. 7 in C Sharp Minor, Op. 64 No. 2; Waltz No. 8 in A Flat Major, Op. 64 No. 3, ROMANTIC side 2

Sonata No. 3 in B Minor, Op. 58 for piano, ROMANTIC CONCERTS side 3 band 1

CHORAL MUSIC:

Bach, *St. Matthew Passion:* Selections, BAROQUE side 4

Bruckner, Mass No. 3 in F Minor ("The Great Mass"): Selections, OPULENT CONCERTS side 8

Buxtehude, "Laudate, pueri," RENAIS-SANCE side 3 band 2

Andrea Gabrieli, "Gloria in excelsis Deo," RENAISSANCE side 1 band 3

Andrea Gabrieli, "Magnificat," RE-NAISSANCE CONCERTS side 3 band 4

Giovanni Gabrieli, "In ecclesiis," RE-NAISSANCE side 1 band 5

Gesualdo, "In Monte Oliveti," RE-NAISSANCE CONCERTS side 2 band 4

Gesualdo, "Jesum tradidit," RENAIS-SANCE CONCERTS side 2 band 5

Haydn, *Mass in Time of War* ("Pauk-enmesse"), ELEGANCE CONCERTS side 6, side 7 band 1

Lassus, "De Profundis" (Psalm 129), RENAISSANCE CONCERTS side 9 band 1

Monteverdi, "Chiome d'oro," RE-NAISSANCE CONCERTS side 2 band 2

Monteverdi, *Gloria,* RENAISSANCE side 4 band 2

Monteverdi, "Zefiro torna," RENAIS-SANCE CONCERTS side 2 band 1

Mozart, "Ave verum Corpus," ELE-GANCE CONCERTS side 2 band 5

Mozart, "Laudate Dominum," ELE-GANCE CONCERTS side 2 band 4

Palestrina, *Missa Papae Marcelli,* RE-NAISSANCE CONCERTS side 9 band 2, side 10

Palestrina, *Stabat Mater,* RENAIS-SANCE side 4 band 1

CHORAL MUSIC: *Continued*

Pérez Bocanegra, "Hanacpachap," SPANISH side 7 band 2

Schoenberg, Six Pieces for Male Chorus, Op. 35, TWENTIETH CONCERTS side 5 band 2

Schütz, "Aus der Tiefe" (Psalm 130), RENAISSANCE CONCERTS side 7 band 1

Verdi, *Requiem Mass,* ROMANTIC CONCERTS side 9, side 10

Victoria, "O Magnum Mysterium," SPANISH CONCERTS side 3 band 4

Vivaldi, *Gloria,* BAROQUE CONCERTS side 9 band 4, side 10

Christmas Concerto (Concerto Grosso in F Major, Op. 6 No. 8), Corelli, BAROQUE side 3 band 1

Christmas Oratorio, SWV. 435A: Excerpts, Schütz, RENAISSANCE side 7

Classical Symphony, Op. 25, Prokofiev, TWENTIETH side 5 band 1

Claveles, Los: "Escena lirica," Serrano, SPANISH CONCERTS side 8 band 3

Colección de Tonadillas, Granados, SPANISH side 3 band 5

"Come again, sweet love doth now invite," Dowland, RENAISSANCE side 2 band 3

"Como la rosa en la güerta," Anon.,

SPANISH CONCERTS side 3 band 1

Concert champêtre, Poulenc, TODAY CONCERTS side 7

Concert Royal No. 2 in D Major, Couperin, BAROQUE CONCERTS side 4 band 4

CONCERTOS:

Bach, Brandenburg No. 2 in F Major, BWV. 1047, BAROQUE side 7 band 2

Bach, in D Minor for Two Violins and Strings, BWV. 1043, BAROQUE CONCERTS side 5 band 1

Bartók, Concerto for Orchestra, TWENTIETH side 3 band 2, side 4

Bartók, No. 3 for Piano and Orchestra, TWENTIETH CONCERTS side 2

Beethoven, No. 4 in G Major, Op. 58 for piano, REVOLUTION side 3 band 2, side 4 band 1

Corelli, *Concerto Grosso* in F Major, Op. 6 No. 9, BAROQUE CONCERTS side 7 band 1

Corelli, *Concerto Grosso* in G Minor, Op. 6 No. 8 ("Christmas"), BAROQUE side 3 band 1

Dvořák, in B Minor, Op. 104 for cello, SLAVIC side 5 band 2, side 6

Handel, *Concerto Grosso* in D Major, Op. 6 No. 5, BAROQUE CONCERTS side 8 band 3

CONCERTOS: *Continued*

Handel, in B Flat Major for Harp and Orchestra, BAROQUE CONCERTS side 2 band 1

Haydn, in E Flat Major for Trumpet, ELEGANCE side 3 band 1

Hindemith, for Horn and Orchestra, TODAY side 3 band 2

Liszt, No. 1 in E Flat Major for Piano, ROMANTIC side 5

Mendelssohn, in E Minor, Op. 64 for violin, ROMANTIC side 4

Mozart, in B Flat Major, K. 191 for bassoon, ELEGANCE CONCERTS side 2 band 1

Mozart, in G Major, K. 453 for piano, ELEGANCE side 5

Poulenc, *Concert champêtre* for harpsichord and orchestra, TODAY CONCERTS side 7

Poulenc, in G Minor for Organ, Strings and Timpani, TODAY side 8

Prokofiev, No. 3 in C Major, Op. 26 for piano, TWENTIETH side 8

Rachmaninoff No. 4 in G Minor, Op. 40 for piano, PRELUDE CONCERTS side 10

Rodrigo, *Concierto de Aranjuez* for guitar and orchestra, SPANISH CONCERTS side 6 band 1

Saint-Saëns, No. 3 in B Minor, Op. 61 for violin, OPULENT CONCERTS side 7

Schumann, in A Minor, Op. 129 for cello, ROMANTIC CONCERTS side 5

Stravinsky, in D Major for String Orchestra, TWENTIETH side 5 band 2

Telemann, in B Flat Major for Three Oboes, Three Violins and Basso Continuo, BAROQUE side 2 band 1

Vivaldi, in A Major for Two Orchestras, BAROQUE CONCERTS side 5 band 4

Vivaldi, in D Major, Op. 10 No. 3 ("Il Gardellino") for flute, BAROQUE side 3 band 2

Vivaldi-Bach, in A Minor for Four Harpsichords and Strings, BWV. 1065, BAROQUE side 2 band 2

Concierto de Aranjuez for guitar and orchestra, Rodrigo, SPANISH CONCERTS side 6 band 1

"¿Con qué la lavaré?" Rodrigo, SPANISH CONCERTS side 6 band 4

Consecration of the House: Overture, Beethoven, REVOLUTION CONCERTS side 1 band 1

"Consort II," Henry VIII, RENAISSANCE CONCERTS side 6 band 5

COPLAND, Aaron:

Appalachian Spring, TODAY side 5

Four Dance Episodes from Rodeo, TO-
DAY CONCERTS side 3 band 2, side
4 band 1

CORELLI, Arcangelo:

Concerto Grosso ir F Major, Op. 6
No. 9, BAROQUE CONCERTS side
7 band 1

Concerto Grosso in G Minor, Op. 6
No. 8 ("Christmas Concerto"),
BAROQUE side 3 band 1

Corte de Faraon, La: "Couplets Babiloni-
cas," Lleó, SPANISH CONCERTS side 8
band 5

COUPERIN, François:

L'Arlequine, BAROQUE side 6 band 1

Les Barricades Mystérieuses, BA-
ROQUE side 6 band 1

Concert Royal No. 2 in D Major, BA-
ROQUE CONCERTS side 4 band 4

*Le Parnasse ou L'Apothéose de Cor-
elli,* BAROQUE CONCERTS side 7
band 2

"Couplets Babilonicos," Lleó, SPANISH
CONCERTS side 8 band 5

Creation, The: Part 1, Haydn, ELEGANCE
side 3 band 2, side 4

Création du monde, La, Milhaud, TWEN-
TIETH side 6 band 3

Cuatro Madrigales Amatorios, Rodrigo,
SPANISH CONCERTS side 6 band 4

Czar Saltan, The Tale of: Opus 57, Rimsky-Korsakov, SLAVIC side 7 band 2

D

Damnation de Faust, La, Op. 24, Berlioz,
ROMANTIC CONCERTS side 6 band 1

"Danse de Puck, La," Debussy, PRELUDE
side 7 band 3

Danzas Fantásticas, Turina, SPANISH side
1 band 2

Daphnis et Chloé: Suite No. 2, Ravel,
PRELUDE side 8 band 2

DEBUSSY, Claude:

Ibéria (Images pour Orchestre, No. 2),
SPANISH CONCERTS side 9 band 2

La Mer, PRELUDE side 5

Nocturnes, PRELUDE CONCERTS side
3

Preludes from Book 1: No. 8, "La Fille
aux cheveux de lin"; No. 10, "La
Cathédrale engloutie"; No. 11, "La
Danse de Puck"; No. 12, "Minstrels"; PRELUDE side 7 band 3

"¿De dónde venís, amore?", Valderrábano, SPANISH side 3 band 3

"¿De dónde venís, amore?", Rodrigo,
SPANISH CONCERTS, side 6 band 4

"De los álamos vengo, madre," Fuenllana, SPANISH side 3 band 3

"De los álamos vengo, madre," Rodrigo,
SPANISH CONCERTS side 6 band 4

"De Profundis" *(Psalm 129),* Lassus, RENAISSANCE CONCERTS side 9 band 1

Dido and Aeneas: Act 3, Closing Scene, Purcell, BAROQUE CONCERTS side 6 band 5

Distressed Innocence: Air, Purcell, BAROQUE side 1 band 5

Don Giovanni: Act 2, Final Scene, Mozart, ELEGANCE side 8

Don Quixote, Richard Strauss, PRELUDE CONCERTS side 1, side 2 band 1

Double Dealer, The: Air, Purcell, BAROQUE side 1 band 5

DOWLAND, John:
    "Come again, sweet love doth now invite," RENAISSANCE side 2 band 3
    "The Right Honourable Lady Rich, Her Galliard," RENAISSANCE CONCERTS side 6 band 2
    "Say Love, if ever thou didst find," RENAISSANCE side 2 band 6
    "Semper Dowland, semper dolens," RENAISSANCE side 2 band 6

"Draw on, sweet night," Wilbye, RENAISSANCE CONCERTS side 6 band 5

DVORAK, Antonín:
    Concerto in B Minor, Op. 104 for cello, SLAVIC side 5 band 2, side 6
    Quartet No. 12 in F Major, Op. 96 ("American") for strings, SLAVIC CONCERTS side 8

Scherzo Capriccioso, Op. 66, SLAVIC CONCERTS side 1 band 1

Slavonic Rhapsody No. 3 in A Flat, Op. 45, SLAVIC side 5 band 1

Symphony No. 8 in G Major, Op. 88, SLAVIC CONCERTS side 1 band 2, side 2

E

"Ecce tempus idoneum," Tallis, RENAISSANCE side 6 band 1

EDWARDS, Richard, "Where griping grief," RENAISSANCE CONCERTS side 6 band 6

Eine Kleine Nachtmusik (Serenade No. 13 in G Major, K. 525), Mozart, ELEGANCE side 2 band 2

ELEGANCE, AGE OF
    Side 1
        Band 1, Boccherini, Overture in D Major, Op. 43
        Bands 2-5, Haydn, Symphony No. 94 in G Major ("Surprise")
    Side 2
        Band 1, Gluck, *Iphigénie en Aulide:* Overture
        Band 2, Mozart, Serenade No. 13 in G Major, K. 525 *(Eine Kleine Nachtmusik)*

Side 3

    Band 1, Haydn, Concerto in E-Flat Major for Trumpet

    Band 2, Haydn, *The Creation:* Part 1: Beginning

    Side 4, Haydn, *The Creation:* Part 1: Conclusion

    Side 5, Mozart, Concerto in G Major, K. 453 for piano

    Side 6, Mozart, Quintet in A Major, K. 581 for clarinet

    Side 7, Beethoven, Symphony No. 1 in C Major, Op. 21

    Side 8, Mozart, *Don Giovanni:* Act 2, Final Scene

ELEGANCE, AGE OF (CONCERTS)

Side 1

    Band 1, Haydn, *Lo Speziale:* Overture

    Bands 2-5, Haydn, Symphony No. 48 in C Major ("Maria Theresia")

Side 2

    Bands 1-3, Mozart, Concerto in B Flat Major, K. 191 for bassoon

    Band 4, Mozart, *Vesperae Solemnes de Confessore,* K. 339: "Laudate Dominum"

    Band 5, Mozart, "Ave verum Corpus," K. 618

Side 3, Beethoven, Sonata No. 5 in F Major, Op. 24 ("Spring") for piano and violin

Side 4

    Band 1, Mozart, Three German Dances, K. 605

    Band 2, Mozart, *The Abduction from the Seraglio:* Act 1, Overture and Aria, "Hier soll ich dich denn sehen"

    Band 3, Mozart, *The Abduction from the Seraglio:* Act 1, "Chorus of Janizaries"

    Band 4, Mozart, *The Abduction from the Seraglio:* Act 1, "Marsch, marsch, marsch"

    Band 5, Mozart, *The Abduction from the Seraglio:* Act 2, Aria, "Matern aller Arten"

Side 5, Mozart, *The Abduction from the Seraglio:* Conclusion

    Band 1, Act 2, Quartet, "Ach Belmonte, ach mein Leben!"

    Band 2, Act 3, Romance, "Im Mohrenland gefangen war," "O, wie will ich triumphieren"

    Band 3, Vaudeville Finale

Side 6, Haydn, *Mass in Time of War* ("Paukenmesse")

    Band 1, Kyrie

    Band 2, Gloria

    Band 3, Credo

    Band 4, Sanctus

Side 7

    Band 1, Haydn, *Mass in Time of*

ELEGANCE, AGE OF (CONCERTS):
Continued

    War ("Paukenmesse"): Benedictus

    Band 2, Haydn, *Mass in Time of War* ("Paukenmesse"): Agnus Dei

    Bands 3-6, Boccherini, Symphony in C Minor

Side 8

    Bands 1-3, Haydn, Sonata No. 35 in C Major for piano

    Bands 4-7, Haydn, Quartet in D Major, Op. 64 No. 5 ("Lark") for strings

Side 9, Gluck, *Iphigénie en Tauride*

    Band 1, Act 1, Recitative, "Dieux! le malheur en tous lieux"; Aria, "De noirs pressentiments"

    Band 2, Act 2, Recitative, "Quel silence effrayant"; Aria, "Dieux! qui me poursuivez"

    Band 3, Aria, "Unis dès la plus tendre enfance"

    Band 4, Aria, "O malheureuse Iphigénie"

    Band 5, Act 3, Aria, "Ah! mon ami"

    Band 6, Aria, "Divinité des grandes âmes"

    Band 7, Act 4, Recitative, "Non, cet affreux devoir"; Aria, "Je t' im-plore et je tremble"

    Band 8, Hymn, "Chaste fille de Latone"

Side 10, Mozart, Symphony No. 39 in E Flat Major, K. 543

Elizabethan Songs and Dances. *See* FROM THE RENAISSANCE side 2

"Emperor" Waltz, Op. 437, Johann Strauss II, OPULENT CONCERTS side 5 band 3

ENCINA, Juan del, "Ay triste que vengo," SPANISH side 3 band 1

Ensembles for Synthesizer, Part I, Babbitt, TODAY side 6 band 1

Eroica Symphony (Symphony No. 3 in E Flat Major, Op. 55), Beethoven, REVOLUTION side 7, side 8

"Escena lirica," Serrano, SPANISH CONCERTS side 8 band 4

España, Chabrier, SPANISH side 4 band 1

"España Vengo, De," Luna, SPANISH side 6 band 1

ESPLA, Oscar, *La Pájara Pinta,* Op. 25: Excerpts, SPANISH CONCERTS side 7 band 1

"Estávase la mora en su bel estar," Anon., SPANISH CONCERTS side 3 band 1

"Evocación," Albéniz, SPANISH side 2 band 1

Execution of Stepan Razin, The, Op. 119, Shostakovich, TODAY side 7

F

Facsimile, Bernstein, TODAY CONCERTS side 4 band 3

Fairy Queen, Music from, Purcell, BAROQUE side 1 band 1

FALLA, Manuel de:
  El Amor Brujo, SPANISH CONCERTS side 10
  "Hommage à Debussy," SPANISH side 3 band 6
  Nights in the Gardens of Spain, SPANISH side 5
  Siete canciones populares españolas: "Jota," "Polo," SPANISH side 3 band 7
  The Three-Cornered Hat, SPANISH side 7 band 3, side 8
  La Vida Breve: Act 2, Scene 1, SPANISH side 1 band 1

Fancy Free: Excerpts, Bernstein, TODAY side 6 band 2

Fantasia in F Major, Z. 745 ("Upon One Note"), Purcell, BAROQUE CONCERTS side 8 band 2

Fantasia No. 9, Mudarra, SPANISH side 3 band 2

Festival Overture, Op. 96, Shostakovich, TODAY side 1 band 1

"Fille au cheveux de lin, La," Debussy, PRELUDE side 7 band 3

Fingal's Cave (The Hebrides Overture), Mendelssohn, ROMANTIC side 1 band 1

Five Pieces for Orchestra, Op. 10, Webern, TWENTIETH CONCERTS side 4 band 1

Flamenco Songs and Dances. *See* THE SPANISH STYLE side 6 band 2

Fledermaus, Die: Overture, Strauss II, OPULENT side 5 band 1

"Fortune my foe," Anon., RENAISSANCE CONCERTS side 6 band 7

Four Pieces for Clarinet and Piano, Op. 5, Berg, TWENTIETH side 2 band 1

Four Sea Interludes, Op. 33A (from *Peter Grimes),* Britten, TODAY side 4 band 2

Freischütz, Der: Overture, Weber, REVOLUTION side 1 band 2

FRESCOBALDI, Girolamo:
  La Bergamasca, RENAISSANCE side 5 band 3
  "Capriccio del soggetto *Fra Jacopin,"* RENAISSANCE CONCERTS side 2 band 3

FUENLLANA, Miguel de, "De los álamos vengo," SPANISH side 3 band 3

"Fuyons tous d'amour le jeu," Lassus, RENAISSANCE side 5 band 2

G

GABRIELI, Andrea:
"Benedictus Dominus," RENAISSANCE CONCERTS side 3 band 1
"Gloria in excelsis Deo," RENAISSANCE side 1 band 3
"Magnificat," RENAISSANCE CONCERTS side 3 band 4
"O crux splendidior," RENAISSANCE CONCERTS side 3 band 2
"Ricercar," RENAISSANCE side 1 band 4

GABRIELI, Giovanni:
"Buccinate in neomenia," RENAISSANCE side 1 band 1
Canzona, RENAISSANCE side 1 band 2
"In ecclesiis," RENAISSANCE side 1 band 5
"Timor et tremor," RENAISSANCE CONCERTS side 3 band 3

Gardellino, Il (Concerto in D Major for flute), Vivaldi, BAROQUE side 3 band 2

Gavotte Variée, Rameau, BAROQUE side 6 band 2

German Dances, Three, K. 605, Mozart, ELEGANCE CONCERTS side 4 band 1

GERSHWIN, George:
An American in Paris, TWENTIETH side 7 band 1
"I Got Rhythm" Variations, TWENTIETH CONCERTS side 3 band 4

GESUALDO, Carlo:
"In Monte Oliveti," RENAISSANCE CONCERTS side 2 band 4
"Jesum tradidit," RENAISSANCE CONCERTS side 2 band 5
"Languisce al fin," RENAISSANCE side 5 band 4

Gianni Schicchi, Puccini, PRELUDE CONCERTS side 8, side 9

Gigantes y Cabezudos: "Romanza de Pilar," Caballero , SPANISH CONCERTS side 8 band 6

"Gigg, A," Byrd, RENAISSANCE side 2 band 4

GIMENEZ, Geronimo, *La Tempranica:* "Zapateado," SPANISH CONCERTS side 8 band 1

GLINKA, Mikhail:
Ivan Susanin: Susanin's Aria, SLAVIC side 1 band 2
Jota aragonesa, SPANISH CONCERTS side 1 band 1
Ruslan and Ludmila: Overture, SLAVIC side 1 band 1
Songs: "The Midnight Review," " 'Grandpa!', The Girls Once Asked Me," "I Remember the Wonderful

Moment," SLAVIC CONCERTS side 7 band 2

Gloria, Monteverdi, RENAISSANCE, side 4 band 2

Gloria, Vivaldi, BAROQUE CONCERTS side 9 band 4, side 10

"Gloria in excelsis Deo," Andrea Gabrieli, RENAISSANCE side 1 band 3

"Gloria tibi Trinitas," Tallis, RENAISSANCE CONCERTS side 1 band 2

GLUCK, Christoph Willibald:
    Iphigénie en Aulide: Overture, ELEGANCE side 2 band 1
    Iphigénie en Tauride: Selections, ELEGANCE CONCERTS side 9

Götterdämmerung: Siegfried's Funeral March, Wagner, OPULENT CONCERTS side 1 band 2

Goyescas, No. 4, Granados, SPANISH side 2 band 4

GRANADOS, Enrique:
    Colección de Tonadillas, SPANISH side 3 band 5
    Goyescas, No. 4, SPANISH side 2 band 4
    Spanish Dance No. 10 in G Major, SPANISH CONCERTS side 2 band 4
    Spanish Dance No. 12 in A minor, SPANISH CONCERTS side 2 band 5

" 'Grandpa!', The Girls Once Asked Me," Glinka, SLAVIC CONCERTS side 7 band 3

Great Mass (No. 3 in F Minor): Credo, Sanctus, Benedictus, Bruckner, OPULENT CONCERTS side 8

Great Symphony (No. 9 in C Major), Schubert, REVOLUTION CONCERTS side 9, side 10

"Guárdame las vacas," Narváez, SPANISH side 3 band 4

"Haec dies," Byrd, RENAISSANCE side 6 band 4

"Hanacpachap," Pérez Bocanegra, SPANISH side 7 band 2

HANDEL, George Frideric:
    Amadigi: Selections, BAROQUE CONCERTS side 6 band 1
    Concerto Grosso in D Major, Op. 6 No. 5, BAROQUE CONCERTS side 8 band 3
    Concerto in B Flat Major for Harp and Orchestra, BAROQUE CONCERTS side 2 band 1
    Messiah: Selections, BAROQUE side 5
    Water Music (Suite in G Major, Suite in D Major), BAROQUE side 8

HARPSICHORD MUSIC:
    Bull, "St. Thomas, Wake," RENAISSANCE CONCERTS side 6 band 4

Couperin, *Concert Royal* No. 2 in D Major, BAROQUE CONCERTS side 4 band 4

Couperin, *Les Barricades Mystérieuses, L'Arlequine,* BAROQUE side 6 band 1

Frescobaldi, "Capriccio del soggetto *Fra Jacopin,*" RENAISSANCE CONCERTS side 2 band 3

Poulenc, *Concert champêtre,* TODAY CONCERTS side 7

Rameau, *Gavotte Variée,* BAROQUE side 6 band 2

Scarlatti, Sonata in A Minor, L. 429, in D Major, L. 164, BAROQUE side 7 band 1

Scarlatti, Sonata in B Flat Major, L. 498, BAROQUE CONCERTS side 4 band 1

Scarlatti, Sonata in B Major, L. 450, BAROQUE CONCERTS side 4 band 3

Scarlatti, Sonata in D Major, L. 461, BAROQUE CONCERTS side 4 band 2

Vivaldi-Bach, Concerto in A Minor for Four Harpsichords and Strings, BAROQUE side 2 band 2

HAYDN, Franz Joseph:
Concerto in E Flat Major for Trumpet, ELEGANCE side 3 band 1

The Creation: Part 1, ELEGANCE side 3 band 2, side 4

Lo Speziale: Overture, ELEGANCE CONCERTS side 1 band 1

Mass in Time of War ("Paukenmesse"), ELEGANCE CONCERTS side 6 band 1, side 7

Quartet in D Major, Op. 64 No. 5 ("Lark") for strings, ELEGANCE CONCERTS side 8 band 4

Sonata No. 35 in C Major for piano, ELEGANCE CONCERTS side 8 band 1

Symphony No. 48 in C Major ("Maria Theresia"), ELEGANCE CONCERTS side 1 band 2

Symphony No. 94 in G Major ("Surprise"), ELEGANCE side 1 band 2

Hebrides, The (Fingal's Cave), Mendelssohn, ROMANTIC side 1 band 1

Henry V: Suite, Walton, TODAY side 1 band 2

HENRY VIII:
"Consort II," RENAISSANCE CONCERTS side 6 band 5

"Pastime with Good Company," RENAISSANCE CONCERTS side 6 band 1

"Herr, nun lässest du deinen Diener," Schütz, RENAISSANCE CONCERTS side 7 band 3

HESSEN, Moritz von, "Pavana del Tomaso di Canosa," RENAISSANCE CONCERTS side 7 band 2

"Hey ho, to the greenwood," Byrd, RE-NAISSANCE CONCERTS side 6 band 8

Hijas del Zebedeo, Las: "Carceleras," Chapí, SPANISH side 6 band 1

HINDEMITH, Paul:

Concerto for Horn and Orchestra, TO-DAY side 3 band 2

Mathis der Maler Symphony, TODAY CONCERTS side 5

Hodie, Vaughan Williams, TODAY CON-CERTS side 9, side 10

"Hommage à Debussy," Falla, SPANISH side 3 band 6

"Hor che'l ciel," Monteverdi, RENAIS-SANCE side 5 band 5

HYMNS & MOTETS:

Byrd, "Ave verum Corpus," RENAIS-SANCE side 6 band 5

Byrd, "Haec dies," RENAISSANCE side 6 band 4

Byrd, "Lamentationes," RENAISSANCE CONCERTS side 1 band 3

Byrd, "O quam gloriosum," RENAIS-SANCE side 6 band 6

Andrea Gabrieli, "Benedictus Domi-nus," RENAISSANCE CONCERTS side 3 band 1

Andrea Gabrieli, "O crux splendidior," RENAISSANCE CONCERTS side 3 band 2

Giovanni Gabrieli, "Buccinate in ne-omenia," RENAISSANCE side 1

band 1

Giovanni Gabrieli, "Timor et tremor," RENAISSANCE CONCERTS side 3 band 3

Lassus, "Iustorum animae," RENAIS-SANCE side 6 band 3

Mozart, "Ave verum Corpus," ELE-GANCE CONCERTS side 2 band 5

Tallis, "Ecce tempus idoneum," RE-NAISSANCE side 6 band 1

Tallis, "Jesu Salvator saeculi," RENAIS-SANCE side 6 band 2

Tallis, "Spem in Alium," RENAIS-SANCE CONCERTS side 1 band 1

Victoria, "O Magnum Mysterium," SPANISH CONCERTS side 3 band 4

Victoria, "Vere languores," "Ave Ma-ria," SPANISH side 7 band 1

I

Iberia: Selections, Albéniz, SPANISH side 2 band 1

Ibéria (Images pour Orchestre, No. 2), Debussy, SPANISH CONCERTS side 9 band 2

"Ich will es nicht achten," Krieger, RE-NAISSANCE CONCERTS side 8 band 6

"I Got Rhythm" Variations, Gershwin,

TWENTIETH CONCERTS side 3 band 4

Images pour Orchestre, No. 2 *(Ibéria),* Debussy, SPANISH CONCERTS side 9 band 2

"Im Krapfenwald'l" Polka, Op. 336, Johann Strauss II, OPULENT CONCERTS side 5 band 2

"In der Fremde," Schumann, ROMANTIC side 6 band 2

Indes galantes, Les: Second Entrée, Rameau, BAROQUE CONCERTS side 6 band 4

Indian Queen, Music from, Purcell, BAROQUE side 1 band 2

"In ecclesiis," Giovanni Gabrieli, RENAISSANCE side 1 band 5

"In Monte Oliveti," Gesualdo, RENAISSANCE CONCERTS side 2 band 4

Intermezzi, Three, Op. 117, Brahms, OPULENT CONCERTS side 3 band 2

"Intermezzo," Schumann, ROMANTIC side 6 band 3

In the Steppes of Central Asia, Borodin, SLAVIC side 1 band 3

Introduction and Allegro, Ravel, PRELUDE side 1 band 2

Introduction and Rondo Capriccioso, Op. 28, Saint-Saëns, OPULENT side 5 band 2

Invitation to the Dance, Op. 65, Weber, REVOLUTION CONCERTS side 4 band 3

Iphigénie en Aulide: Overture, Gluck, ELEGANCE side 2 band 1

Iphigénie en Tauride: Selections, Gluck, ELEGANCE CONCERTS side 9

"I Remember the Wonderful Moment," Glinka, SLAVIC CONCERTS side 7 band 4

Islamey ("Oriental Fantasy"), Balakirev, SLAVIC side 1 band 4

Italian Girl in Algiers, The: Overture, Rossini, REVOLUTION CONCERTS side 5 band 1

"Iustorum animae," Lassus, RENAISSANCE side 6 band 3

Ivan Susanin: Susanin's Aria, Glinka, SLAVIC side 1 band 2

J

"Jägerlied," Schubert, REVOLUTION CONCERTS side 7 band 1

JANACEK, Leoš:
Sinfonietta, SLAVIC side 8
Wind Sextet *(Mládí),* SLAVIC CONCERTS side 4 band 1

"Jesum tradidit," Gesualdo, RENAISSANCE CONCERTS side 2 band 5

"Jesu Salvator saeculi," Tallis, RENAISSANCE side 6 band 2

Jeux d'eau, Ravel, PRELUDE side 7 band 2

Jota aragonesa, Glinka, SPANISH CONCERTS side 1 band 1

K

"Kemp's Jig," Anon., RENAISSANCE side 2 band 7

King Arthur, Music from, Purcell, BAROQUE side 1 band 2

Klavierstücke ("Piano Pieces"), Op. 33A and 33B, Schoenberg, TWENTIETH side 6 band 1

Kleine Nachtmusik, Eine (Serenade No. 13 in G Major, K. 525), Mozart, ELEGANCE side 2 band 2

Knaben Wunderhorn, Des, Songs from, Mahler, PRELUDE side 8 band 1

KRIEGER, Adam, "Ich will es nicht achten," RENAISSANCE CONCERTS side 8 band 6

L

LALO, Edouard, *Symphonie espagnole,* Op. 21, SPANISH CONCERTS side 4, side 5 band 1

"Lamentationes" ("The Lamentations of Jeremiah the Prophet"), Byrd, RENAISSANCE CONCERTS side 1 band 3

"Languisce al fin," Gesualdo, RENAISSANCE side 5 band 4

Lark Ascending, The, Vaughan Williams, TODAY CONCERTS side 3 band 1

Lark Quartet (Quartet in D Major, Op. 34 No. 5), Haydn, ELEGANCE CONCERTS side 8 band 4

LASSUS, Roland de:
"De Profundis" (Psalm 129), RENAISSANCE CONCERTS side 9 band 1
"Iustorum animae," RENAISSANCE side 6 band 3
"Quand mon mari vient de dehors," "Fuyons tous d'amour le jeu," RENAISSANCE side 5 band 2

"Laudate Dominum," Mozart, ELEGANCE CONCERTS side 2 band 4

"Laudate, pueri," Buxtehude, RENAISSANCE side 3 band 2

Leipzig, Sonatas and Songs of. *See* FROM THE RENAISSANCE CONCERTS side 8, band 5

Leonore Overture No. 3, Op. 72, Beethoven, REVOLUTION side 1 band 1

"Let Us Wander," Purcell, BAROQUE side 1 band 3

Liederkreis, Op. 39: Selections, Schumann, ROMANTIC side 6 band 2

"L'Ile inconnue," Berlioz, ROMANTIC CONCERTS side 4 band 5

LISZT, Franz:

  Années de Pèlerinage: Selections, ROMANTIC CONCERTS side 7

  Concerto No. 1 in E Flat Major for piano, ROMANTIC side 5

  Les Préludes, ROMANTIC side 1 band 2

LLEO, Vicente, *La Corte de Faraón:* "Couplets Babilonicos," SPANISH CONCERTS side 8 band 5

Lohengrin: Bridal Chamber Scene, Wagner, OPULENT CONCERTS side 6

Los de Aragón: "Romanza de Gloria," Serrano, SPANISH CONCERTS side 8 band 2

Lo Speziale: Overture, Haydn, ELEGANCE CONCERTS side 1 band 1

"Lost is My Quiet," Purcell, BAROQUE side 1 band 2

LULLY, Jean Baptiste:

  Les Amants magnifiques: Suite, RENAISSANCE side 3 band 3

  Ballet de la Nuit: Selections, RENAISSANCE CONCERTS side 8 band 3

  Ballet d'Hercule: Selections, RENAISSANCE CONCERTS side 8 band 2

Lulu: Excerpts, Berg, TWENTIETH CONCERTS side 4 band 2

LUNA, Pablo, *El Niño Judío:* "De España vengo," SPANISH side 6 band 1

M

Macbeth: Sleepwalking Scene, Verdi, ROMANTIC side 3 band 2

MADRIGALS:

  Byrd, "This Sweet and Merry Month," RENAISSANCE side 2 band 5

  Gesualdo, "Languisce al fin," RENAISSANCE side 5 band 4

  Monteverdi, "Hor che'l ciel," RENAISSANCE side 5 band 5

  Weelkes, "Sing we at pleasure," RENAISSANCE side 2 band 1

  Wilbye, "Adieu, sweet Amaryllis," RENAISSANCE side 2 band 8

  Wilbye, "Draw on, sweet night," RENAISSANCE CONCERTS side 6 band 5

"Magnificat," Andrea Gabrieli, RENAISSANCE CONCERTS side 3 band 4

MAHLER, Gustav:

  Songs from *Des Knaben Wunderhorn,* PRELUDE side 8 band 1

  Symphony No. 2 in C Minor ("Resurrection"), PRELUDE CONCERTS side 4, side 5, side 6, side 7

  Symphony No. 4 in G Major, PRELUDE side 3, side 4

Manfred Overture, Op. 115, Schumann,

ROMANTIC CONCERTS side 1 band 1

"Maravillosos e piadosos," Alfonso El Sabio, SPANISH CONCERTS side 3 band 2

"Marche de triomphe," Charpentier, RENAISSANCE CONCERTS side 8 band 1

Mass in Time of War ("Paukenmesse"), Haydn, ELEGANCE CONCERTS side 6, side 7 band 1

Mass No. 3 in F Minor ("Great"): Credo, Sanctus and Benedictus, Bruckner, OPULENT CONCERTS side 8

Mathis der Maler Symphony, Hindemith, TODAY CONCERTS side 5

"Matica de ruda, Una," Anon., SPANISH side 3 band 1

Mazurka No. 17 in B Flat Minor, Op. 24 No. 4, Chopin, ROMANTIC side 2 band 1

"Mein Herz ist bereit," Buxtehude, RENAISSANCE CONCERTS side 7 band 5

Meistersinger von Nürnberg, Die: Prelude, Wagner, OPULENT side 1 band 1

MENDELSSOHN, Felix:

Concerto in E Minor, Op. 64 for violin, ROMANTIC side 4

The Hebrides Overture, Op. 26 *(Fingal's Cave),* ROMANTIC side 1 band 1

Octet in E Flat Major for Strings, Op. 20, ROMANTIC CONCERTS side 8

Symphony No. 3 in A Minor, Op. 56 ("Scotch"), ROMANTIC CONCERTS side 1 band 2, side 2

Mer, La, Debussy, PRELUDE side 5

Messiah: Selections, Handel, BAROQUE side 5

"Midnight Review, The," Glinka, SLAVIC CONCERTS side 7 band 2

MILAN, Luis, Pavane No. 5, SPANISH side 3 band 2

MILHAUD, Darius:

La Création du monde, TWENTIETH side 6 band 3

Suite française, TWENTIETH CONCERTS side 5 band 1

"Minstrels," Debussy, PRELUDE side 7 band 3

Missa Papae Marcelli, Palestrina, RENAISSANCE CONCERTS side 9 band 2, side 10

Mlada: Selections, Rimsky-Korsakov, SLAVIC CONCERTS side 3

Mládí (Wind Sextet), Janáček, SLAVIC CONCERTS side 4 band 1

Moldau, The, Smetana, SLAVIC side 2 band 1

"Mondnacht," Schumann, ROMANTIC side 6 band 6

MONTEVERDI, Claudio:

Il Ballo delle Ingrate: Ballet Music, RENAISSANCE side 5 band 6

"Chiome d'oro," RENAISSANCE CONCERTS side 2 band 2

Gloria, RENAISSANCE side 4 band 2

"Hor che'l ciel," RENAISSANCE side 5 band 5

L'Incoronazione di Poppea: Excerpts, RENAISSANCE side 8

Orfeo: Act 2, Act 3, RENAISSANCE CONCERTS side 4, side 5

"Zefiro torna," RENAISSANCE CONCERTS side 2 band 1

"Morgenstern, Der," Schubert, REVOLUTION CONCERTS side 7 band 3

MORLEY, Thomas, "Now is the month of Maying," RENAISSANCE CONCERTS side 6 band 3

MOTETS. *See* HYMNS AND MOTETS

MOUSSORGSKY, Modest:

    Boris Godounov: Scenes, SLAVIC side 3, side 4

    Moussorgsky-Ravel, *Pictures at an Exhibition,* SLAVIC CONCERTS side 4 band 5, side 5

MOZART, Wolfgang Amadeus:

    The Abduction from the Seraglio: Selections, ELEGANCE CONCERTS side 4 band 2, side 5

    "Ave verum Corpus," K. 618, ELEGANCE CONCERTS side 2 band 5

    Concerto in B Flat Major, K. 191 for bassoon, ELEGANCE CONCERTS side 2 band 1

    Concerto in G Major, K. 453 for piano, ELEGANCE side 5

Don Giovanni: Act 2, Final Scene, ELEGANCE side 8

Quintet in A Major, K. 581 for clarinet, ELEGANCE side 6

Serenade No. 13 in G Major, K. 525 *(Eine Kleine Nachtmusik),* ELEGANCE side 2 band 2

Symphony No. 39 in E Flat Major, K. 543, ELEGANCE CONCERTS side 10

Three German Dances, K. 605, ELEGANCE CONCERTS side 4 band 1

Vesperae Solemnes de Confessore, K. 339: "Laudate Dominum," ELEGANCE CONCERTS side 2 band 4

MUDARRA, Alonso de, Fantasia No. 9 for vihuela, SPANISH side 3 band 2

MUNDY, John, "Robin," RENAISSANCE side 2 band 4

Music for String Instruments, Percussion and Celesta, Bartók, TWENTIETH CONCERTS side 7

N

"Nacht, Die," Schubert, REVOLUTION CONCERTS side 7 band 1

"Nachthelle," Schubert, REVOLUTION CONCERTS side 7 band 3

NARVAEZ, Luis de:

    Variations on "Guárdame las vacas,"

SPANISH side 3 band 4

"Paseábase el rey moro," SPANISH CONCERTS side 3 band 3

"Negritos, Los," Araujo, SPANISH side 7 band 1

Night Pieces, Schubert, REVOLUTION CONCERTS side 7 band 1

Nights in the Gardens of Spain, Falla, SPANISH side 5

Niño Judío, El: "De España vengo," Luna, SPANISH side 6 band 1

Nocturnes, Debussy, PRELUDE CONCERTS side 3

"Now is the month of Maying," Morley, RENAISSANCE CONCERTS side 6 band 3

Nuits d'été, Les, Berlioz, ROMANTIC CONCERTS side 3 band 5, side 4

Oberon: Excerpts, Weber, REVOLUTION CONCERTS side 6

"O crux splendidior," Andrea Gabrieli, RENAISSANCE CONCERTS side 3 band 2

Octet in E Flat Major for Strings, Op. 20, Mendelssohn, ROMANTIC CONCERTS side 8

OFFENBACH, Jacques:

Orpheus in the Underworld: Overture, OPULENT side 3 band 1

The Tales of Hoffmann: Act 2, OPULENT CONCERTS side 4

"Oft have I sighed," Campion, RENAISSANCE side 2 band 3

"O Magnum Mysterium," Victoria, SPANISH CONCERTS side 3 band 4

OPERAS:

Abduction from the Seraglio, The: Selections, Mozart, ELEGANCE CONCERTS side 4 band 2, side 5

Amadigi: Selections, Handel, BAROQUE CONCERTS side 6 band 1

Ballo in Maschera, Un: Selections, Verdi, ROMANTIC side 3 band 3

Barber of Seville, The: Selections, Rossini, REVOLUTION side 5

Bartered Bride, The: Overture, Smetana, SLAVIC side 7 band 1; Act 3, SLAVIC CONCERTS side 9, side 10

Bohème, La: Act 3, Puccini, PRELUDE side 6

Boris Godounov: Scenes, Moussorgsky, SLAVIC side 3, side 4

Carmen: Act 4, Bizet, SPANISH side 4 band 2

Dido and Aeneas: Act 3, Closing Scene, Purcell, BAROQUE CONCERTS side 6 band 5

Don Giovanni: Act 2, Final Scene, Mozart, ELEGANCE side 8

OPERAS: *Continued*

Fledermaus, Die: Overture, Strauss II, OPULENT side 5 band 1

Freischütz, Der: Overture, Weber, REVOLUTION side 1 band 2

Gianni Schicchi, Puccini, PRELUDE CONCERTS side 8, side 9

Götterdämmerung: Siegfried's Funeral March, Wagner, OPULENT CONCERTS side 1 band 2

Incoronazione di Poppea, L': Scenes, Monteverdi, RENAISSANCE side 8

Indes galantes, Les: Second Entrée, Rameau, BAROQUE CONCERTS side 6 band 4

Iphigénie en Aulide: Overture, Gluck, ELEGANCE side 2 band 1

Iphigénie en Tauride: Selections, Gluck, ELEGANCE CONCERTS side 9

Italian Girl in Algiers, The: Overture, Rossini, REVOLUTION CONCERTS side 5 band 1

Ivan Susanin: Susanin's Aria, Glinka, SLAVIC side 1 band 2

Lohengrin: Bridal Chamber Scene, Wagner, OPULENT CONCERTS side 6

Lo Speziale: Overture, Haydn, ELEGANCE CONCERTS side 1 band 1

Lulu: Excerpts, Berg, TWENTIETH CONCERTS side 4 band 2

Macbeth: Sleepwalking Scene, Verdi, ROMANTIC side 3 band 2

Meistersinger, Die: Prelude, Wagner, OPULENT side 1 band 1

Mlada: Selections, Rimsky-Korsakov, SLAVIC CONCERTS side 3

Oberon: Excerpts, Weber, REVOLUTION CONCERTS side 6

Orfeo: Act 2 and Act 3, Monteverdi, RENAISSANCE CONCERTS side 4, side 5

Orpheus in the Underworld: Overture, Offenbach, OPULENT side 3 band 1

Peter Grimes: Four Sea Interludes, Britten, TODAY side 4 band 2

Prince Igor: Polovtsian Dances, Borodin, SLAVIC CONCERTS side 6 band 1

Púrpura de la rosa, La: Nymph's Chorus and Loa, Torrejón y Velasco, SPANISH CONCERTS side 3 band 5

Rosenkavalier, Der: Selections, Richard Strauss, PRELUDE side 2

Ruslan and Ludmila: Overture, Glinka, SLAVIC side 1 band 1

Semiramide: Overture, Rossini, REVOLUTION CONCERTS side 5 band 3

Tale of Czar Saltan, The: Suite, Op. 57, Rimsky-Korsakov, SLAVIC side 7 band 2

Tales of Hoffmann, The: Act 2, Offenbach, OPULENT CONCERTS side 4

Traviata, La: Selections, Verdi, ROMANTIC side 3 band 4

Tristan und Isolde: Prelude and Liebestod, Wagner, OPULENT CONCERTS side 1 band 1

Trovatore, Il: Selections, Verdi, ROMANTIC side 3 band 1

Troyens, Les: Royal Hunt and Storm, Berlioz, ROMANTIC CONCERTS side 6 band 2

Vida Breve, La: Act 2, Scene 1, Falla, SPANISH side 1 band 1

Walküre, Die: Act 2, Scene 3, Wagner, OPULENT side 4

William Tell: Ballet Music, Rossini, REVOLUTION CONCERTS side 5 band 2

OPULENT ERA, THE
Side 1
Band 1, Wagner, *Die Meistersinger von Nürnberg:* Prelude
Band 2, Brahms, Symphony No. 2 in D Major, Op. 73: Beginning
Side 2, Brahms, Symphony No. 2 in D Major, Op. 73: Conclusion
Side 3
Band 1, Offenbach, *Orpheus in the Underworld:* Overture
Band 2, Tchaikovsky, *Romeo and Juliet* Fantasy Overture

Side 4, Wagner, *Die Walküre:* Act 3, Scene 3
Side 5
Band 1, Johann Strauss II, *Die Fledermaus:* Overture
Band 2, Saint-Saëns, Introduction and Rondo Capriccioso, Op. 28
Band 3, Brahms, *Academic Festival Overture,* Op. 80
Side 6, Tchaikovsky, *Swan Lake,* Op. 20: Suite
Band 1, Swan Theme
Band 2, Waltz, Act 1
Band 3, Dance of the Little Swans, Act 2
Band 4, Pas de Deux, Act 2
Band 5, Hungarian Dance (Czardas), Act 3
Side 7, Bruckner, Symphony No. 4 in E Flat Major ("Romantic"). Beginning
Side 8, Bruckner, Symphony No. 4 in E Flat Major ("Romantic"): Conclusion
OPULENT ERA, THE (CONCERTS)
Side 1
Band 1, Wagner, *Tristan und Isolde:* Prelude and Liebestod
Band 2, Wagner, *Götterdämmerung:* Siegfried's Funeral March
Side 2, Brahms, Sextet No. 1 in B Flat Major, Op. 18 for strings: Beginning

OPULENT ERA, THE (CONCERTS):
Continued
Side 3
    Band 1, Brahms, Sextet No. 1 in B
    Flat Major, Op. 18 for strings:
    Conclusion
    Band 2, Brahms, *Three Intermezzi,*
    Op. 117: No. 1 in E Flat Major
    Band 3, Brahms, *Three Intermezzi,*
    Op. 117: No. 2 in B Flat Major
    Band 4, Brahms, *Three Intermezzi,*
    Op. 117: No. 3 in C Sharp Minor
Side 4, Offenbach, *The Tales of Hoff-
mann (Les Contes d'Hoffmann):*
Act 2 ("A Venise")
Side 5
    Band 1, Johann Strauss II, "Tales
    from the Vienna Woods" Waltz,
    Op. 325
    Band 2, Johann Strauss II, "Im
    Krapfenwald'l" Polka, Op. 336
    Band 3, "Emperor" Waltz, Op. 437
Side 6, Wagner, *Lohengrin:* Act 3,
Bridal Chamber Scene
Side 7, Saint-Saëns, Concerto No. 3 in
B Minor, Op. 61 for violin
Side 8, Bruckner, Mass No. 3 in F
Minor ("The Great Mass"): Selec-
tions
    Band 1, Credo
    Band 2, Sanctus
    Band 3, Benedictus

Side 9, Tchaikovsky, Symphony No. 5
in E Minor, Op. 64: Beginning
Side 10, Tchaikovsky, Symphony No. 5
in E Minor, Op. 64: Conclusion
"O quam gloriosum," Byrd, RENAIS-
SANCE side 6 band 6
Oración del torero, La, Turina, SPANISH
CONCERTS side 7 band 2
Orfeo: Act 2 and Act 3, Monteverdi, RE-
NAISSANCE CONCERTS side 4, side 5
ORGAN MUSIC:
    Bach, Toccata and Fugue in D Minor,
    BWV. 565, BAROQUE side 6 band 3
    Bach, Trio Sonata No. 5 in C Major,
    BAROQUE CONCERTS side 9 band
    1
    Buxtehude, "Ach Herr, mich armen
    Sünder," RENAISSANCE CON-
    CERTS side 7 band 4
    Buxtehude, Prelude and Fugue in G
    Minor, RENAISSANCE side 3 band 1
    Frescobaldi, *La Bergamasca,* RENAIS-
    SANCE side 5 band 3
    Poulenc, Concerto in G Minor for
    Organ, Strings and Timpani, TO-
    DAY side 8
    Tallis, "Gloria tibi Trinitas," RENAIS-
    SANCE CONCERTS side 1 band 2
"Oriental Fantasy" *(Islamey),* Balakirev,
SLAVIC side 1 band 4
Orpheus in the Underworld: Overture,
Offenbach, OPULENT side 3 band 1

ORTEGA, Francisco, "Pues que me tienes, Miguel," SPANISH CONCERTS side 3 band 3

P

Pájara Pinta, La: Excerpts, Op. 25, Esplá, SPANISH CONCERTS side 7 band 1

PALESTRINA, Giovanni Pierluigi da:
  Missa Papae Marcelli, RENAISSANCE CONCERTS side 9 band 2, side 10
  Stabat Mater, RENAISSANCE side 4 band 1

Papillons, Op. 2, Schumann, ROMANTIC side 6 band 1

Partita for Orchestra, Walton, TODAY CONCERTS side 1 band 1

"Paseábase el rey moro," Narváez, SPANISH CONCERTS side 3 band 3

"Pastime with Good Company," Henry VIII, RENAISSANCE CONCERTS side 6 band 1

"Pastorcico non te aduermas," Anon., SPANISH side 3 band 1

Paukenmesse (Mass in Time of War), Haydn, ELEGANCE CONCERTS side 6, side 7 band 1

"Pavana del Tomaso di Canora," Moritz von Hessen, RENAISSANCE CON-CERTS side 7 band 2

Pavane No. 9, Milán, SPANISH side 3 band 2

PEREZ BOCANEGRA, Juan, "Hanacpa-chap," SPANISH side 7 band 2

Peter Grimes: Four Sea Interludes, Britten, TODAY side 4 band 2

PEZEL, Johann, Sonata No. 39, RENAIS-SANCE CONCERTS side 8 band 6

PIANO MUSIC:
  Albéniz, *Iberia:* Selections, SPANISH side 2 band 1
  Albéniz, "Preludio," SPANISH CON-CERTS side 2 band 2
  Albéniz, "Serenata Española," Op. 181, SPANISH CONCERTS side 2 band 3
  Albéniz, "Sevilla," SPANISH CON-CERTS side 2 band 1
  Bartók, Concerto No. 3 for Piano and Orchestra, TWENTIETH CONCERTS side 2
  Beethoven, Concerto No. 4 in G Major, REVOLUTION side 3 band 2, side 4 band 1
  Beethoven, Sonata No. 5 in F Major, Op. 24 ("Spring") for violin and piano, ELEGANCE CONCERTS side 3
  Beethoven, Sonata No. 27 in E Minor, REVOLUTION side 4 band 2
  Brahms, *Three Intermezzi,* Op. 117, OPULENT CONCERTS side 3 band 2

PIANO MUSIC: *Continued*

Chopin, Mazurka No. 17 in B Flat Minor, Op. 24 No. 4; Polonaise No. 3 in A Major, Op. 40 No. 1; Ballade No. 1 in G Minor, Op. 23; Waltz No. 6 in D Flat Major, Op. 64 No. 1; Waltz No. 7 in C Sharp Minor, Op. 64 No. 2; Waltz No. 8 in A Flat Major, Op. 64 No. 3, ROMANTIC side 2

Chopin, Sonata No. 3 in B Minor, Op. 58, ROMANTIC CONCERTS side 3 band 1

Debussy, Four Preludes from Book 1: No. 8, "La Fille au Cheveux de lin," No. 10, "La Cathédrale engloutie," No. 11, "La Danse de Puck," No. 12, "Minstrels," PRELUDE side 7 band 3

Gershwin, *"I Got Rhythm" Variations,* TWENTIETH CONCERTS side 3 band 4

Granados, *Goyescas,* No. 4: "Quejas o la maja y el ruiseñor," SPANISH side 2 band 4

Granados, Spanish Dance No. 10 in G Major, SPANISH CONCERTS side 2 band 4

Granados, Spanish Dance No. 12 in A Minor, SPANISH CONCERTS side 2 band 5

Haydn, Sonata No. 35 in C Major,

ELEGANCE CONCERTS side 8 band 1

Liszt, *Années de Pèlerinage:* Selections, ROMANTIC CONCERTS side 7

Liszt, Concerto in E Flat Major, ROMANTIC side 5

Mozart, Concerto in G Major, K. 453, ELEGANCE side 5

Prokofiev, Concerto No. 3 in C Major, Op. 26, TWENTIETH side 8

Rachmaninoff, Concerto No. 4 in G Minor, Op. 40, PRELUDE CONCERTS side 10

Rachmaninoff, Preludes in G Minor, Op 23 No. 5; in G Major, Op. 32 No. 5; in G Sharp Minor, Op. 32 No. 12, PRELUDE side 7 band 1

Ravel, *Jeux d'eau,* PRELUDE side 7 band 2

Schubert, Quintet in A Major, Op. 114 ("Trout") for piano and strings, REVOLUTION CONCERTS side 3, side 4 band 1

Schoenberg, *Klavierstücke* (Piano Pieces), Op. 33A and 33B, TWENTIETH side 6 band 1

Schumann, *Papillons,* Op. 2, ROMANTIC side 6 band 1

Turina, *Rapsodia sinfonica,* SPANISH CONCERTS side 7 band 3

Weber, *Invitation to the Dance,* Op.

65, REVOLUTION CONCERTS side 4 band 3

Pictures at an Exhibition, Moussorgsky-Ravel, SLAVIC CONCERTS side 4 band 5, side 5

"Polovtsian Dances," *Prince Igor,* Borodin, SLAVIC CONCERTS side 6 band 1

Polonaise No. 3 in A Major, Op. 40 No. 1, Chopin, ROMANTIC side 2 band 2

Poppea, L'Incoronazione di: Scenes, Monteverdi, RENAISSANCE side 8

POULENC, Francis:

Concert champêtre, TODAY CONCERTS side 7

Concerto in G Minor for Organ, Strings and Timpani, TODAY side 8

Prelude and Fugue in G Minor, Buxtehude, RENAISSANCE side 3 band 1

Préludes, Les, Liszt, ROMANTIC side 1 band 2

PRELUDE TO MODERN MUSIC

Side 1

Band 1, Richard Strauss, *Till Eulenspiegel*

Band 2, Ravel, Introduction and Allegro

Side 2, Richard Strauss, *Der Rosenkavalier:* Selections

Band 1, Act 2: Presentation of the Silver Rose

Band 2, Act 2: Finale

Band 3, Act 3: Trio and Duet

Side 3, Mahler, Symphony No. 4 in G Major: Beginning

Side 4, Mahler, Symphony No. 4 in G Major: Conclusion

Side 5, Debussy, *La Mer*

Band 1, "De l'aube à midi sur la mer"

Band 2, "Jeux de vagues"

Band 3, "Dialogue du vent et de la mer"

Side 6, Puccini, *La Bohème:* Act 3

Side 7

Band 1, Rachmaninoff, Preludes in G Minor, Op. 23 No. 5; in G Major, Op. 32 No. 5; in G Sharp Minor, Op. 32 No. 12

Band 2, Ravel, *Jeux d'eau*

Band 3, Debussy, Four Preludes from Book 1: No. 8, "La Fille aux cheveux de lin," No. 10, "La Cathédrale engloutie," No. 11, "La Danse de Puck," No. 12, "Minstrels"

Side 8

Band 1, Mahler, Songs from *Des Knaben Wunderhorn:* "Revelge," "Wer hat dies Liedlein erdacht?", "Lob des hohen Verstandes"

Band 2, Ravel, *Daphnis et Chloé:* Suite No. 2

PRELUDE TO MODERN MUSIC (CON-
CERTS)
Side 1, Richard Strauss, *Don Quixote,*
Op. 35: Beginning
Side 2
Band 1, Richard Strauss, *Don Quix-*
ote, Op. 35: Conclusion
Band 2, Ravel, *La Valse*
Side 3, Debussy, *Nocturnes*
Band 1, "Nuages"
Band 2, "Fêtes"
Band 3, "Sirènes"
Side 4, Mahler, Symphony No. 2 in C
Minor ("Resurrection"): First
Movement
Side 5, Mahler, Symphony No. 2 in C
Minor ("Resurrection"): Continued
Band 1, Second Movement
Band 2, Third Movement
Side 6, Mahler, Symphony No. 2 in C
Minor ("Resurrection"): Fourth
Movement and Fifth Movement
(beginning)
Side 7, Mahler, Symphony No. 2 in C
Minor ("Resurrection"): Fifth
Movement *(conclusion)*
Side 8, Puccini, *Gianni Schicchi:* Be-
ginning
Side 9, Puccini, *Gianni Schicchi:* Con-
clusion
Side 10, Rachmaninoff, Concerto No. 4
in G Minor, Op. 40 for piano

"Preludio," Albéniz, SPANISH CON-
CERTS side 2 band 2
Prince Igor: Polovtsian Dances, Borodin,
SLAVIC CONCERTS side 6 band 1
PROKOFIEV, Sergei:
Alexander Nevsky, Op. 78 TWENTI-
ETH CONCERTS side 8, side 9
band 1
Classical Symphony, Op. 25 (Sym-
phony No. 1 in D Major), TWENTI-
ETH side 5 band 1
Concerto No. 3 in C Major, Op. 26
for piano, TWENTIETH side 8
Symphony No. 5 in B Flat Major, Op.
100, TWENTIETH CONCERTS side 9
band 3, side 10
Psalm 129 ("De Profundis"), Lassus, RE-
NAISSANCE CONCERTS side 9 band 1
Psalm 130 ("Aus der Tiefe"), Schütz, RE-
NAISSANCE CONCERTS side 7 band 1
PUCCINI, Giacomo:
La Bohème: Act 3, PRELUDE side 6
Gianni Schicchi, PRELUDE CONCERTS
side 8, side 9
"Pues que me tienes, Miguel," Ortega,
SPANISH CONCERTS side 3 band 3
Pulcinella: Suite, Stravinsky, TWENTIETH
CONCERTS side 1
PURCELL, Henry:
Dido and Aeneas: Act 3, Closing
Scene, BAROQUE CONCERTS side
6 band 5

Fantasia in F Major, Z. 745 ("Upon One Note"), BAROQUE CONCERTS side 8 band 2

Theater Music and Songs: Music from *The Fairy Queen*, Music from *The Indian Queen*, "Let Us Wander," "Lost Is My Quiet," Music from *King Arthur, Abdelazer, Distressed Innocence, Amphitryon, The Double Dealer*, BAROQUE side 1

Trio Sonata in G Major, Z. 797, BAROQUE CONCERTS side 8 band 1

Púrpura de la rosa, La: Nymphs' Chorus and Loa, Torréjon y Velasco, SPANISH CONCERTS side 3 band 5

Q

"Quand mon mari vient de dehors," Lassus, RENAISSANCE side 5 band 2

Quartet in D Major, Op. 64 No. 5 ("Lark") for strings, Haydn, ELEGANCE CONCERTS side 8 band 4

Quartet No. 12 in F Major, Op. 96 ("American") for strings, Dvořák, SLAVIC CONCERTS side 8

Quartet No. 16 in F Major, Op. 135 for strings, Beethoven, REVOLUTION side 6

Quintet in A Major, K. 581 for clarinet, Mozart, ELEGANCE side 6

Quintet in A Major, Op. 114 ("Trout") for piano and strings, Schubert, REVOLUTION CONCERTS side 3, side 4 band 1

R

RACHMANINOFF, Sergei:

Concerto No. 4 in G Minor, Op. 40 for piano, PRELUDE CONCERTS side 10

Preludes in G Minor, Op. 23 No. 5; in G Major, Op. 32 No. 5; in G Sharp Minor, Op. 32 No. 12 for piano, PRELUDE side 7 band 1

RAMEAU, Jean Philippe:

Gavotte Variée for harpsichord, BAROQUE side 6 band 2

Les Indes galantes: Second Entrée, BAROQUE CONCERTS side 6 band 4

Rapsodia sinfonica, Turina, SPANISH CONCERTS side 7 band 3

Rapsodie espagnole, Ravel, SPANISH CONCERTS side 5 band 2

RAVEL, Maurice:

Alborada del Gracioso, SPANISH CONCERTS side 9 band 1

Daphnis et Chloé: Suite No. 2, PRE-LUDE side 8 band 2

Introduction and Allegro, PRELUDE side 1 band 2

Jeux d'eau, PRELUDE side 7 band 2

Moussorgsky-Ravel, *Pictures at an Exhibition,* SLAVIC CONCERTS side 4 band 5, side 5

Rapsodie espagnole, SPANISH CONCERTS side 5 band 2

La Valse, PRELUDE CONCERTS side 2 band 2

RENAISSANCE, FROM THE

Side 1, Ceremonial Music of Venice by Andrea and Giovanni Gabrieli

    Band 1, Giovanni Gabrieli, "Buccinate in neomenia"

    Band 2, Giovanni Gabrieli, "Canzona"

    Band 3, Andrea Gabrieli, "Gloria in excelsis Deo"

    Band 4, Andrea Gabrieli, "Ricercar"

    Band 5, Giovanni Gabrieli, "In ecclesiis"

Side 2, Elizabethan Songs and Dances

    Band 1, Weelkes, "Sing we at pleasure"

    Band 2, Anon., "Almaine," "Scots Marche"

    Band 3, Campion, "Oft have I sighed"; Dowland, "Come again"

    Band 4, Mundy, "Robin"; Byrd, "A Gigg"

    Band 5, Byrd, "This Sweet and Merry Month"

    Band 6, Dowland, "Semper Dowland, semper dolens," "Say Love, if ever thou didst find"

    Band 7, Anon., "Watkin's Ale," "Kemp's Jig"

    Band 8, Wilbye, "Adieu, sweet Amaryllis"

Side 3

    Band 1, Buxtehude, Prelude and Fugue in G Minor

    Band 2, Buxtehude, "Laudate, pueri"

    Band 3, Lully, *Les Amants magnifiques:* Suite

Side 4

    Band 1, Palestrina, *Stabat Mater*

    Band 2, Monteverdi, *Gloria*

Side 5, Madrigals, Chansons and Instrumental Music

    Band 1, Susato, "Rondo and Saltarello," "Allemainge"

    Band 2, Lassus, "Quand mon mari," "Fuyons tous d'amour le jeu"

    Band 3, Frescobaldi, *La Bergamasca*

    Band 4, Gesualdo, "Languisce al fin"

    Band 5, Monteverdi, "Hor che'l ciel"

RENAISSANCE, FROM THE: *(Continued)*
    Band 6, Monteverdi, *Il Ballo delle Ingrate:* Ballet Music
  Side 6, Hymns and Motets
    Band 1, Tallis, "Ecce tempus idoneum"
    Band 2, Tallis, "Jesu Salvator saeculi"
    Band 3, Lassus, "Iustorum animae"
    Band 4, Byrd, "Haec dies"
    Band 5, Byrd, "Ave verum Corpus"
    Band 6, Byrd, "O quam gloriosum"
  Side 7, Schütz, *The Christmas Oratorio,* SWV: 435A: Excerpts ("Da nun Jesus geboren war," Interlude 4: "Wo ist der neugeborne König der Juden," "Da das der König Herodes hörete," Interlude 5: "Zu Bethlehem im jüdischen Lande," "Da berief Herodes," Interlude 6: "Ziehet hin," "Als sie nun den König," Interlude 7: "Stehe auf Joseph," "Und er stund auf," Interlude 8: "Stehe auf, Joseph," "Und er stund auf," Conclusion: "Dank sagen wir alle, alle Gott")
  Side 8, Monteverdi, *L'Incoronazione di Poppea:* Excerpts
    Band 1, Act 1, Sinfonia
    Band 2, Act 1, "Come dolci, Signor"
    Band 3, Act 1, "Amici è giunta l'hora" (Death of Seneca)

    Band 4, Act 2, "Hor che Seneca è morto"
    Band 5, Act 2, "A te, a te sovrana augusta" (Coronation Scene)
RENAISSANCE, FROM THE (CONCERTS)
  Side 1
    Band 1, Tallis, "Spem in alium" (40-Part Motet)
    Band 2, Tallis, "Gloria tibi Trinitas"
    Band 3, Byrd, "Lamentationes"
  Side 2
    Band 1, Monteverdi, "Zefiro torna"
    Band 2, Monteverdi, "Chiome d'oro"
    Band 3, Frescobaldi, "Capriccio del soggetto *Fra Jacopin* scritto sopra l'aria de *Ruggiero*"
    Band 4, Gesualdo, "In Monte Oliveti"
    Band 5, Gesualdo, "Jesum tradidit"
  Side 3, Music for St. Mark's by Andrea and Giovanni Gabrieli
    Band 1, Andrea Gabrieli, "Benedictus Dominus"
    Band 2, Andrea Gabrieli, "O crux splendidior"
    Band 3, Giovanni Gabrieli, "Timor et tremor"
    Band 4, Andrea Gabrieli, "Magnificat"
  Side 4, Monteverdi, *Orfeo:* Act 2
  Side 5, Monteverdi, *Orfeo:* Act 3

RENAISSANCE, FROM THE (CONCERTS):
Continued

Side 6, Songs and Dances of Tudor England

Band 1, Henry VIII, "Pastime with Good Company"; Anon., "Bransle"

Band 2, Campion, "Shall I come sweet love to thee"; Dowland, "The Right Honourable Lady Rich, Her Galliard"

Band 3, Morley, "Now is the month of Maying"

Band 4, Bull, "St. Thomas, Wake"

Band 5, Henry VIII, "Consort II"; Wilbye, "Draw on, sweet night"

Band 6, Edwards, "Where griping grief"

Band 7, Anon., "Fortune My Foe"

Band 8, Tomkins, "Worcester Brawls"; Byrd, "Hey ho, to the greenwood"

Side 7

Band 1, Schütz, "Aus der Tiefe" (Psalm 130)

Band 2, Moritz von Hessen, "Pavana del Tomaso di Canora"

Band 3, Schütz, "Herr, nun lässest de deinen Diener"

Band 4, Buxtehude, "Ach Herr, mich armen Sünder" (Organ Chorale)

Band 5, Buxtehude, "Mein Herz ist bereit"

Side 8, Marches and Ballet Music for Versailles; Sonatas and Songs of Leipzig

Band 1, Charpentier, "Marche de triomphe"

Band 2, Lully, *Ballet d'Hercule:* "Apollon entouré des douze heures du jour"; "Le Roy, ou la septième influence"

Band 3, Lully, *Ballet de la Nuit:* "Dialogue du sommeil et du silence"; "Le Roy représentant le Soleil levant"

Band 4, Charpentier, "Second Air de Trompettes"

Band 5, Rosenmüller, *Sinfonia undecima*

Band 6, Pezel, Wind Sonata No. 39; Krieger, "Ich will es nicht achten"; Theile, "Was acht' ich deine Gunst?"

Side 9

Band 1, Lassus, "De Profundis" (Psalm 129 from "Penitential Psalms")

Band 2, Palestrina, *Missa Papae Marcelli* (Mass of Pope Marcellus): Kyrie

Band 3, Palestrina, *Missa Papae Marcelli:* Gloria

Side 10, Palestrina, *Missa Papae Marcelli:* Conclusion
Band 1, Credo
Band 2, Sanctus
Band 3, Benedictus
Band 4, Agnus Dei
Requiem Mass: Excerpts, Verdi, ROMANTIC CONCERTS side 9, side 10
Resurrection Symphony (Symphony No. 2 in C Minor), Mahler, PRELUDE CONCERTS side 4, side 5, side 6, side 7

REVOLUTION, AGE OF
Side 1
Band 1, Beethoven, *Leonore Overture No. 3,* Op. 72
Band 2, Weber, *Der Freischütz:* Overture
Side 2, Schubert, Symphony No. 5 in B Flat Major, D. 485
Side 3
Band 1, Schubert, Songs from *Die schöne Müllerin,* D. 795: "Wohin?", "Der Neugierige Mein!" "Trockne Blumen"
Band 2, Beethoven, Concerto No. 4 in G Major, Op. 58 for piano: Beginning
Side 4
Band 1, Beethoven, Concerto No. 4 in G Major, Op. 58 for piano: Conclusion

Band 2, Beethoven, Sonata No. 27 in E Minor, Op. 90 for piano
Side 5, Rossini, *The Barber of Seville*
Band 1, Act 1, "Largo al factotum"
Band 2, Act 1, "Una voce poco fa"
Band 3, Act 1, "La calunnia"
Band 4, Act 1, "Dunque io son"
Band 5, Act 2, "Buona sera"
Band 6, Act 2, Finale, "Di si felice innesto"
Side 6, Beethoven, Quartet No. 16 in F Major, Op. 135 for strings
Side 7, Beethoven, Symphony No. 3 in E Flat Major, Op. 55 ("Eroica"): Beginning
Side 8, Beethoven, Symphony No. 3 in E Flat Major, Op. 55 ("Eroica"): Conclusion

REVOLUTION, AGE OF (CONCERTS)
Side 1
Band 1, Beethoven, *The Consecration of the House* Overture, Op. 124
Band 2, Beethoven, Symphony No. 4 in B Flat Major, Op. 60: Beginning
Side 2, Beethoven, Symphony No. 4 in B Flat Major, Op. 60: Conclusion
Side 3, Schubert, Quintet in A Major, Op. 114 ("Trout") for piano and strings: Beginning

REVOLUTION, AGE OF (CONCERTS):
Continued
Side 4
  Bands 1-2, Schubert, Quintet in A Major, Op. 114 ("Trout"): Conclusion
  Band 3, Weber, *Invitation to the Dance,* Op. 65
Side 5
  Band 1, Rossini, *The Italian Girl in Algiers:* Overture
  Band 2, Rossini, *William Tell:* Ballet Music ("Passo a tre" and "Coro Tirolese")
  Band 3, Rossini, *Semiramide:* Overture
Side 6, Weber, *Oberon:* Excerpts
  Band 1, Overture
  Band 2, Act 1, "Von Jugend auf in dem Kampfgefild"
  Band 3, Act 2, "Vater! Hör' mich fleh'n zu dir!"
  Band 4, Act 2, "Ozean, du Ungeheuer!"
Side 7
  Band 1, Schubert, Night Pieces: "Jägerlied," "Die Nacht"
  Band 2, Schubert, Night Pieces: "Ständchen"
  Band 3, Schubert, Night Pieces: "Nachthelle,""Der Morgenstern"
  Band 4, Beethoven, Trio in B Flat Major, Op. 97 ("Archduke"): Beginning
Side 8, Beethoven, Trio in B Flat Major, Op. 97 ("Archduke"): Conclusion
Side 9, Schubert, Symphony No. 9 in C Major ("The Great"), D. 944: Beginning
Side 10, Schubert, Symphony No. 9 in C Major ("The Great"), D. 944: Conclusion
"Ricercar," Andrea Gabrieli, RENAISSANCE side 1 band 4
"Right Honourable Lady Rich, Her Galliard, The," Dowland, RENAISSANCE CONCERTS side 6 band 2
RIMSKY-KORSAKOV, Nicolai:
  Capriccio Espagnol, Op. 34, SPANISH CONCERTS side 1 band 2
  Mlada: Selections, SLAVIC CONCERTS side 3
  "Russian Easter" Overture, Op. 36, SLAVIC side 2 band 2
  The Tale of Czar Saltan: Suite, Op. 57, SLAVIC side 7 band 2
"Robin," Mundy, RENAISSANCE side 2 band 4
Rodeo, Four Dance Episodes from, Copland, TODAY CONCERTS side 3 band 2, side 4 band 1
RODRIGO, Joaquín:
  Concierto de Aranjuez for guitar and

orchestra, SPANISH CONCERTS side 6 band 1

Cuatro Madrigales Amatorios, SPANISH CONCERTS side 6 band 4

ROMANTIC ERA, THE

Side 1

Band 1, Mendelssohn, *The Hebrides* Overture, Op. 26 *(Fingal's Cave)*

Band 2, Liszt, *Les Préludes* (Symphonic Poem)

Side 2, Chopin, Piano Compositions

Band 1, Mazurka No. 17 in B Flat Minor, Op. 24 No. 4

Band 2, Polonaise No. 3 in A Major, Op. 40 No. 1

Band 3, Ballade No. 1 in G Minor, Op. 23

Band 4, Waltz No. 6 in D Flat Major, Op. 64 No. 1; Waltz No. 7 in C Sharp Minor, Op. 64 No. 2; Waltz No. 8 in A Flat Major, Op. 64 No. 3

Side 3, Verdi, Operatic Selections

Band 1, *Il Trovatore:* Act 4, "Miserere" ("Ah! che la morte")

Band 2, *Macbeth:* Act 4, "Una macchia è qui tuttora" (Sleepwalking Scene)

Band 3, *Un Ballo in Maschera:* Act 3, "Eri tu, che macchiavi"

Band 4, *La Traviata:* Act 1, "Ah! fors' è lui," "Sempre libera"

Side 4, Mendelssohn, Concerto in E Minor, Op. 64 for violin

Side 5, Liszt, Concerto in E Flat Major for piano

Side 6

Band 1, Schumann, *Papillons,* Op. 2

Band 2, Schumann, *Liederkreis,* Op. 39: "In der Fremde"

Band 3, Schumann, *Liederkreis,* Op. 39: Intermezzo

Band 4, Schumann, *Liederkreis,* Op. 39: "Waldesgespräch"

Band 5, Schumann, *Liederkreis,* Op. 39: "Die Stille"

Band 6, Schumann, *Liederkreis,* Op. 39: "Mondnacht"

Side 7, Berlioz, *Symphonie fantastique:* Beginning

Band 1, First Movement: "Reveries-Passions"

Band 2, Second Movement: "A Ball"

Band 3, Third Movement, "Scene in the Country" *(beginning)*

Side 8, Berlioz, *Symphonie fantastique:* Conclusion

Band 1, Third Movement, "Scene in the Country *(conclusion)*

Band 2, Fourth Movement, "March to the Scaffold"

Band 3, Fifth Movement, "Witches Sabbath"

ROMANTIC ERA, THE (CONCERTS)
Side 1
    Band 1, Schumann, *Manfred,* Op. 115: Overture
    Band 2, Mendelssohn, Symphony No. 3 in A Minor, Op. 56 ("Scotch"): Beginning
Side 2, Mendelssohn, Symphony No. 3 in A Minor, Op. 56 ("Scotch"): Conclusion
Side 3
    Bands 1-4, Chopin, Sonata No. 3 in B Minor, Op. 58 for piano
    Band 5, Berlioz, *Les Nuits d'été:* "Villanelle"
Side 4, Berlioz, *Les Nuits d'été:* Conclusion
    Band 1, "Le Spectre de la rose"
    Band 2, "Sur les Lagunes"
    Band 3, "Absence"
    Band 4, "Au Cimetière"
    Band 5, "L'Ile inconnue"
Side 5, Schumann, Concerto in A Minor, Op. 129 for cello
Side 6
    Band 1, Berlioz, *Le Damnation de Faust,* Op. 24: Part 1
    Band 2, Berlioz, *Les Troyens:* Royal Hunt and Storm
Side 7, Liszt, *Années de Pèlerinage*
    Band 1, *Première année: La Suisse,* "Au Lac de Wallenstadt"

Band 2, "Pastorale"
Band 3, "Au Bord d'une source"
Band 4, "Eglogue"
Band 5, "Le Mal du pays"
Band 6, *Deuxième année: L'Italie,* "Sonetto 104 del Petrarca"
Band 7, "Sonetto 123 del Petrarca"
Side 8, Mendelssohn, Octet in E Flat Major for Strings, Op. 20
Side 9, Verdi, *Requiem Mass:* Dies irae *(beginning)*
Side 10, Verdi, *Requiem Mass*
    Band 1, Dies irae *(conclusion)*
    Band 2, Agnus Dei
    Band 3, Lux aeterna
Romantic Symphony (Symphony No. 4 in E Flat Major), Bruckner, OPULENT side 7, side 8
"Romanza de Gloria," Serrano, SPANISH CONCERTS side 8 band 2
"Romanza de Pilar," Caballero, SPANISH CONCERTS side 8 band 6
Romeo and Juliet Fantasy Overture, Tchaikovsky, OPULENT side 3 band 2
"Rondo," Susato, RENAISSANCE side 5 band 1
"Rosa das rosas," Alfonso El Sabio, SPANISH CONCERTS side 3 band 2
Rosenkavalier, Der: Selections, Richard Strauss, PRELUDE side 2
ROSENMULLER, Johann, *Sinfonia undecima,* RENAISSANCE CONCERTS

side 8 band 5

ROSSINI, Gioacchino:

The Barber of Seville: Selections, REVOLUTION side 5

The Italian Girl in Algiers (L'Italiana in Algeri): Overture, REVOLUTION CONCERTS side 5 band 1

Semiramide: Overture, REVOLUTION CONCERTS side 5 band 3

William Tell: Ballet Music, REVOLUTION CONCERTS side 5 band 2

Ruslan and Ludmila: Overture, Glinka, SLAVIC side 1 band 1

"Russian Easter" Overture, Op.36, Rimsky-Korsakov, SLAVIC side 2 band 2

S

Sacre du Printemps, Le, Stravinsky, TWENTIETH side 2 band 2, side 3 band 1

St. Mark's, Music for, by Andrea and Giovanni Gabrieli. *See* FROM THE RENAISSANCE CONCERTS side 3

St. Matthew Passion: Selections, Bach, BAROQUE side 4

SAINT-SAENS, Camille:

Concerto No. 3 in B Minor, Op. 61 for violin, OPULENT CONCERTS side 7

Introduction and Rondo Capriccioso,

Op. 28 for violin, OPULENT side 5 band 2

"St. Thomas, Wake," Bull, RENAISSANCE CONCERTS side 6 band 4

"Saltarello," Susato, RENAISSANCE side 5 band 1

"Say Love, if ever thou didst find," Dowland, RENAISSANCE side 2 band 6

SCARLATTI, Domenico:

Sonatas for Harpsichord: in A Minor, L. 429; in D Major, L. 164, BAROQUE side 7 band 1

Sonatas for Harpsichord: in B Flat Major, L. 498 (K. 202); in D Major, L. 461 (K. 29); in B Major, L. 450 (K. 425), BAROQUE CONCERTS side 4 band 1

Scherzo Capriccioso, Op. 66, Dvořák, SLAVIC CONCERTS side 1 band 1

SCHOENBERG, Arnold:

Piano Pieces *(Klavierstücke),* Op. 33A and 33B, TWENTIETH side 6 band 1

Six Pieces for Male Chorus, Op. 35, TWENTIETH CONCERTS side 5 band 2

Verklärte Nacht, Op. 4, TWENTIETH side 1

Schöne Müllerin, Die, Songs from, Schubert, REVOLUTION side 3 band 1

SCHUBERT, Franz:

Night Pieces, REVOLUTION CONCERTS side 7 band 1

Quintet in A Major, Op. 114 ("Trout")
for piano and strings, D. 667, REV-
OLUTION CONCERTS side 3, side 4
band 1
Songs from *Die Schöne Müllerin*, D.
795, REVOLUTION side 3 band 1
Symphony No. 5 in B Flat Major, D.
485, REVOLUTION side 2
Symphony No. 9 in C Major ("The
Great"), D. 944, REVOLUTION
CONCERTS side 9, side 10
SCHUMANN, Robert:
Concerto in A Minor, Op. 129 for
cello, ROMANTIC CONCERTS side
5
Manfred, Op. 115: Overture, RO-
MANTIC CONCERTS side 1 band 1
Papillons, Op. 2, ROMANTIC side 6
band 1
Songs from *Liederkreis*, Op. 39, RO-
MANTIC side 6 band 2
SCHUTZ, Heinrich:
"Aus der Tiefe" (Psalm 130), RENAIS-
SANCE CONCERTS side 7 band 1
The Christmas Oratorio, SWV. 435A:
Excerpts, RENAISSANCE side 7
"Herr, nun lässest du deinen Diener,"
RENAISSANCE CONCERTS side 7
band 3
Scotch Symphony (No. 3 in A Minor,
Op. 56), Mendelssohn, ROMANTIC
CONCERTS side 1 band 2, side 2

"Scots Marche," Anon., RENAISSANCE
side 2 band 2
"Second Air de Trompettes," Charpen-
tier, RENAISSANCE CONCERTS side 8
band 4
Semiramide: Overture, Rossini, REVOLU-
TION CONCERTS side 5 band 3
"Semper Dowland, semper dolens,"
Dowland, RENAISSANCE side 2 band 6
"Serenata Española," Op. 181, Albéniz,
SPANISH CONCERTS side 2 band 3
SERRANO, José:
Alegria del Batallon, La: "Canción de
la Gitana," SPANISH CONCERTS
side 8 band 4
Los de Aragón: "Romanza de Gloria,"
SPANISH CONCERTS side 8 band 2
Los Claveles: "Escena lirica," SPANISH
CONCERTS side 8 band 3
"Sevilla," Albéniz, SPANISH CONCERTS
side 2 band 1
Sextet No. 1 in B Flat Major, Op. 18 for
strings, Brahms, OPULENT CONCERTS
side 2, side 3 band 1
"Shall I come sweet love to thee," Cam-
pion, RENAISSANCE CONCERTS side
6 band 2
SHOSTAKOVICH, Dmitri:
The Execution of Stepan Razin, Op.
119, TODAY side 7
Festival Overture, Op. 96, TODAY
side 1 band 1

Symphony No. 9, Op. 70, TODAY
  CONCERTS side 8
Siete canciones populares españoles:
  "Jota," "Polo," Falla, SPANISH side 3
  band 7
Sinfonia undecima, Rosenmüller, RE-
  NAISSANCE CONCERTS side 8 band 5
Sinfonietta, Janáček, SLAVIC side 8
"Sing we at pleasure," Weelkes, RENAIS-
  SANCE side 2 band 1
Six Pieces for Male Chorus, Op. 35,
  Schoenberg, TWENTIETH CONCERTS
  side 5 band 2
SLAVIC TRADITIONS
  Side 1
    Band 1, Glinka, *Ruslan and Lud-
      mila:* Overture
    Band 2, *Ivan Susanin:* Act 4, Scene
      2, Susanin's Aria
    Band 3, Borodin, *In the Steppes of
      Central Asia*
    Band 4, Balakirev, *Islamey* ("Ori-
      ental Fantasy")
  Side 2
    Band 1, Smetana, *The Moldau
      (Vltava)*
    Band 2, Rimsky-Korsakov, *"Russian
      Easter"* Overture, Op. 36
  Side 3, Moussorgsky, *Boris God-
    ounov:* Scenes: Beginning
    Band 1, Prologue: Coronation
      Scene

Band 2, Act 2: Feodor's Narrative,
  Clock Scene
Side 4, Moussorgsky, *Boris God-
  ounov:* Scenes: Conclusion
  Band 1, Act 4: Death of Boris
  Band 2, Act 4: Revolutionary Scene
Side 5
  Band 1, Dvořák, *Slavonic Rhapsody
    No. 3 in A Flat,* Op. 45
  Band 2, Dvořák, Concerto in B
    Minor, Op. 104 for cello: Be-
    ginning
Side 6, Dvořák, Concerto in B Minor,
  Op. 104 for cello: Conclusion
Side 7
  Band 1, Smetana, *The Bartered
    Bride:* Overture
  Band 2, Rimsky-Korsakov, *The Tale
    of Czar Saltan:* Suite, Op. 57
    ("The Czar's Departure and Fare-
    well," "The Czarina in a Barrel
    at Sea," "The Three Wonders")
Side 8, Janáček, *Sinfonietta*
SLAVIC TRADITIONS (CONCERTS)
  Side 1
    Band 1, Dvořák, *Scherzo Capric-
      cioso,* Op. 66
    Band 2, Dvořák, Symphony No. 8 in
      G Major, Op. 88: Beginning
  Side 2, Dvořák, Symphony No. 8 in G
    Major, Op. 88: Conclusion
  Side 3, Rimsky-Korsakov, *Mlada*

49

SLAVIC TRADITIONS (CONCERTS):
Continued
    Band 1, Act 2, "Procession of the
        Nobles"
    Band 2, Act 2, "Kolo"
    Band 3, Act 3, "Witches' Sabbath
        and Infernal Kolo"
    Band 4, Act 4, Final Chorus
Side 4
    Bands 1-4, Janáček, Wind Sextet
        (Mládí)
    Band 5, Moussorgsky-Ravel, *Pic-
        tures at an Exhibition:* "Prom-
        enade," "Gnomus," "Prome-
        nade," "Il vecchio castello"
Side 5, Moussorgsky-Ravel, *Pictures at
    an Exhibition:* "Promenade," "Tuil-
    eries," "Bydlo," "Promenade,"
    "Ballet of the Unhatched Chicks,"
    "Samuel Goldenberg and
    Schmuyle," "Limoges: the Market,"
    "Catacombae," "Cum mortuis in
    lingua mortua," "The Hut on Fowl's
    Legs," "The Great Gate of Kiev"
Side 6
    Band 1, Borodin, *Prince Igor:* Pol-
        ovtsian Dances
    Bands 2-3, Borodin, Symphony No.
        2 in B Minor: Beginning
Side 7
    Band 1, Borodin, Symphony No. 2
        in B Minor: Conclusion

    Band 2, Glinka, "The Midnight Re-
        view"
    Band 3, Glinka, " 'Grandpa!', The
        Girls Once Asked Me"
    Band 4, Glinka, "I Remember the
        Wonderful Moment"
Side 8, Dvořák, Quartet No. 12 in F
    Major, Op. 96 ("American") for
    strings
Side 9, Smetana, *The Bartered Bride*,
    Act 3: Beginning
Side 10, Smetana, *The Bartered Bride*,
    Act 3: Conclusion
Slavonic Rhapsody No. 3 in A Flat, Op.
    45, Dvořák, SLAVIC side 5 band 1
Sleepers Awake (Wachet Auf), Bach, BA-
    ROQUE CONCERTS side 2 band 3,
    side 3
SMETANA, Bedřich:
    The Bartered Bride: Act 3, SLAVIC
        CONCERTS side 9, side 10
    The Bartered Bride: Overture, SLAVIC
        side 7 band 1
    The Moldau (Vltava), SLAVIC side 2
        band 1
Soleil des Eaux, Le, Boulez, TODAY side
    4 band 1
SONATAS:
    Bach, Trio Sonata No. 5 in C Major for
        Organ, BWV. 529, BAROQUE CON-
        CERTS side 9 band 1
    Beethoven, No. 5 in F Major, Op. 24

("Spring") for piano and violin, ELEGANCE CONCERTS side 3

Beethoven, No. 27 in E Minor, Op. 90 for piano, REVOLUTION side 4 band 2

Chopin, No. 3 in B Minor, Op. 58 for piano, ROMANTIC CONCERTS side 3 band 1

Haydn, No. 35 in C Major for piano, ELEGANCE CONCERTS side 8 band 1

Pezel, No. 39, RENAISSANCE CONCERTS side 8 band 6

Purcell, Trio Sonata in G Major, Z. 797, BAROQUE CONCERTS side 8 band 1

Scarlatti, for harpsichord, in A Minor, L. 429; in D Major, L. 164, BAROQUE side 7 band 1; in B Flat Major, L. 498 (K. 202), BAROQUE CONCERTS side 4 band 1; in D Major, L. 461 (K. 29), BAROQUE CONCERTS side 4 band 2; in B Major, L. 450 (K. 245), BAROQUE CONCERTS side 4 band 3

SONGS:

Berlioz, *Les Nuits d'été*, Op. 7, ROMANTIC CONCERTS side 3 band 5, side 4

Glinka, Three Songs, SLAVIC CONCERTS side 7 band 2

Krieger, "Ich will es nicht achten," RENAISSANCE CONCERTS side 8 band 6

Lassus, "Quand mon mari vient de dehors," "Fuyons tous d'amour le jeu," RENAISSANCE side 5 band 2

Mahler, *Des Knaben Wunderhorn*: Selections, PRELUDE side 8 band 1

Purcell, "Let Us Wander," "Lost Is My Quiet," BAROQUE side 1 band 3

Schubert, Night Pieces, REVOLUTION CONCERTS side 7 band 1

Schubert, Songs from *Die Schöne Müllerin*, REVOLUTION side 3 band 1

Schumann, Songs from *Liederkreis*, Op. 39, ROMANTIC side 6 band 2

Theile, "Was acht' ich deine Gunst?", RENAISSANCE CONCERTS side 8 band 6

Webern, Three Songs, Op. 23, TWENTIETH side 6 band 2

See also MADRIGALS; FROM THE RENAISSANCE side 2 (Elizabethan Songs and Dances); FROM THE RENAISSANCE CONCERTS side 6 (Songs and Dances of Tudor England); THE SPANISH STYLE side 3 (Vocal and Guitar Music); side 6 (Zarzuela Arias, Flamenco Songs and Dances); THE SPANISH STYLE CONCERTS, side 3 (Ancient

SONGS: *Continued*
 Andalusian Songs); side 8 (Zarzuela Selections)
Spanish Dance No. 10 in G Major, Granados, SPANISH CONCERTS side 2 band 4
Spanish Dance No. 12 in A Minor, Granados, SPANISH CONCERTS side 2 band 5
SPANISH STYLE, THE
 Side 1
  Band 1, Falla, *La Vida Breve:* Act 2, Scene 1
  Band 2, Turina, *Danzas Fantásticas:* "Exaltación,""Ensueño,""Orgía"
 Side 2
  Band 1, Albéniz, *Iberia:* "Evocación"
  Band 2, Albéniz, *Iberia:* "Triana"
  Band 3, Albéniz, *Iberia:* "El Albaicín"
  Band 4, Granados, *Goyescas,* No. 4: "Quejas o la maja y el ruiseñor"
 Side 3, Vocal and Guitar Music, Ancient and Modern
  Band 1, Anon., "Una matica de ruda"; "Pastorcico non te aduermas"; Encina, "Ay triste que vengo"
  Band 2, Mudarra, Fantasia No. 9; Milán, Pavane No. 5

Band 3, Fuenllana, "De los álamos vengo, madre"; Valderrábano, "¿De dónde venis, amore?"
Band 4, Narváez, Variations on "Guárdame las vacas"
Band 5, Granados, *Colección de Tonadillas:* "El majo timido," "El mirar de la maja," "El tra-lalá y el punteado"
Band 6, Falla, "Hommage à Debussy"
Band 7, Falla, *Siete canciones populares españolas:* "Jota," "Polo"
 Side 4
  Band 1, Chabrier, *España*
  Band 2, Bizet, *Carmen:* Act 4
 Side 5, Falla, *Nights in the Gardens of Spain*
 Side 6, Zarzuela Arias; Flamenco Songs and Dances
  Band 1, Luna, *El Niño Judío:* "De España vengo"; Chapí, *Las Hijas del Zebedeo:* "Carceleras"
  Band 2, Anon., "Sevillanas," "Chirigotas de Cádiz," "Seguiriyas y Soleá," "Fandangos de Almería," "Farruca," "Alegrías"
 Side 7
  Band 1, Victoria, "Vere Languores," "Ave Maria"
  Band 2, Pérez Bocanegra, "Han-

SPANISH STYLE, THE: *Continued*
    acpachap''; Araujo, "Los Negri-
    tos"
  Band 3, Falla, *The Three-Cornered
    Hat:* Introduction and Part 1
  Side 8, Falla, *The Three-Cornered Hat:*
    Part 2
SPANISH STYLE, THE (CONCERTS)
  Side 1
    Band 1, Glinka, *Jota aragonesa*
    Band 2, Rimsky-Korsakov, *Capric-
      cio Espagnol,* Op. 34
  Side 2
    Band 1, Albéniz, "Sevilla" (No. 3 of
      Suite Española)
    Band 2, Albéniz, "Preludio"
    Band 3, Albéniz, "Serenata Es-
      pañola," Op. 181
    Band 4, Granados, Spanish Dance
      No. 10 in G Major
    Band 5, Granados, Spanish Dance
      No. 12 in A Minor
  Side 3, Ancient Andalusian Songs;
    Choral Music from the Old and
    New Worlds
    Band 1, Anon., "Ah, el novio no
      quiere dinero"; "Como la rosa
      en la güerta"; "Estávase la mora
      en su bel estar" *(Canciones
      sefarditas)*
    Band 2, Alfonso El Sabio, "Rosa das
      rosas''; "Maravillosos e pia-

    dosos" *(Cantigas)*
    Band 3, Narváez, "Paseábase el rey
      moro" *(Romance);* Ortega,
      "Pues que me tienes, Miguel"
      (Villancico)
    Band 4, Victoria, "O Magnum
      Mysterium" (Motet)
    Band 5, Torréjon y Velasco, *La
      Púrpura de la Rosa:* Nymphs'
      Chorus and Loa
  Side 4, Lalo, *Symphonie Espagnole,*
    Op. 21: Beginning
  Side 5
    Band 1, Lalo, *Symphonie Espagnole,*
      Op. 21: Conclusion
    Band 2, Ravel, *Rapsodie espagnole:*
      "Prélude à la nuit," "Malagueña"
    Band 3, Ravel, *Rapsodie espagnole:*
      "Habañera"
    Band 4, Ravel, *Rapsodie espagnole:*
      "Feria"
  Side 6
    Bands 1-3, Rodrigo, *Concierto de
      Aranjuez* for guitar and orches-
      tra
    Band 4, Rodrigo, *Cuatro Madrigales
      Amatorios:* "¿Con qué la la-
      varé?," "Vos me matásteis,"
      "¿De dónde venis, amore?," "De
      los álamos vengo, madre"
  Side 7
    Band 1, Esplá, *La Pájara Pinta,* Op.

SPANISH STYLE, THE (CONCERTS):
Continued
25: Excerpts: "Pasa el Conde de Cabra," "Baile de Anton Pirulero," "Berceuse," "Pasodoble de Lepe"
Band 2, Turina, *La Oración del torero*
Band 3, Turina, *Rapsodia Sinfonica*
Side 8, Zarzuela Selections
Band 1, Giménez, *La Tempranica:* "Zapateado"
Band 2, Serrano, *Los de Aragón:* "Romanza de Gloria"
Band 3, Serrano, *La Alegría del Batallon:* "Canción de la Gitana"
Band 4, Serrano, *Los Claveles:* "Escena lirica"
Band 5, Lleó, *La Corte de Faraón:* "Couplets Babilonicos"
Band 6, Caballero, *Gigantes y Cabezudos:* "Romanza de Pilar"
Band 7, Barbieri, *El Barberillo de Lavapiés:* "Canción de Paloma"
Side 9
Band 1, Ravel, *Alborada del Gracioso* (No. 4 of "Miroirs")
Band 2, Debussy, *Ibéria (Images pour Orchestre No. 2):* "Par les rues et par les chemins"
Band 3, Debussy, *Ibéria:* "Les par-fums de la nuit," "Le matin d'un jour de fête"
Side 10, Falla, *El Amor Brujo (Love, the Magician)*
Spectre de la rose, Le, Berlioz, ROMANTIC CONCERTS side 4 band 1
"Spem in Alium," Tallis, RENAISSANCE CONCERTS side 1 band 1
Spring Sonata (No. 5 in F Major, Op. 24), Beethoven, ELEGANCE CONCERTS side 3
Stabat Mater, Palestrina, RENAISSANCE side 4 band 1
"Ständchen," Schubert, REVOLUTION CONCERTS side 7 band 2
"Stille, Die," Schumann, ROMANTIC side 6 band 5
STRAUSS, Johann II:
Die Fledermaus: Overture, OPULENT side 5 band 1
"Emperor" Waltz, Op. 437, OPULENT CONCERTS side 5 band 3
"Im Krapfenwald'l" Polka, Op. 336, OPULENT CONCERTS side 5 band 2
"Tales from the Vienna Woods" Waltz, Op. 325, OPULENT CONCERTS side 5 band 1
STRAUSS, Richard:
Don Quixote, Op. 35, PRELUDE side 1, side 2 band 1

Der Rosenkavalier: Selections, PRE-
LUDE side 2

Till Eulenspiegels Lustige Streiche, Op.
28, PRELUDE side 1 band 1

STRAVINSKY, Igor:

Concerto in D Major for String Orchestra, TWENTIETH side 5 band 2

Pulcinella: Suite, TWENTIETH CON-
CERTS side 1

Le Sacre du Printemps, TWENTIETH
side 2 band 2, side 3 band 1

Symphony in Three Movements,
TWENTIETH CONCERTS side 6

Suite française, Milhaud, TWENTIETH
CONCERTS side 5 band 1

Suite in C Major ("Water Music"), Telemann, BAROQUE CONCERTS side 1

Suite in D Major ("Water Music"), Handel, BAROQUE side 8 band 2

Suite in G Major ("Water Music"), Handel, BAROQUE side 8 band 1

"Sur les Lagunes," Berlioz, ROMANTIC
CONCERTS side 4 band 2

Surprise Symphony (No. 94 in G Major),
Haydn, ELEGANCE side 1 band 2

SUSATO, Tielman, "Rondo and Saltarello," "Allemainge," RENAISSANCE
side 5 band 1

Swan Lake, Op. 20: Suite, Tchaikovsky,
OPULENT side 6

Symphonie espagnole, Op. 21, Lalo,

SPANISH CONCERTS side 4, side 5
band 1

Symphonie fantastique, Berlioz, RO-
MANTIC side 7, side 8

SYMPHONIES:

Beethoven, No. 1 in C Major, Op. 21,
ELEGANCE side 7

Beethoven, No. 3 in E Flat Major, Op.
55 ("Eroica"), REVOLUTION side 7,
side 8

Beethoven, No. 4 in B Flat Major, Op.
60, REVOLUTION CONCERTS side
1 band 2, side 2

Berlioz, *Symphonie fantastique,* RO-
MANTIC side 7, side 8

Boccherini, in C Minor, ELEGANCE
CONCERTS side 7 band 3

Borodin, No. 2 in B Minor, SLAVIC
CONCERTS side 6 band 2, side 7
band 1

Brahms, No. 2 in D Major, Op. 73,
OPULENT side 1 band 2, side 2

Bruckner, No. 4 in E Flat Major ("Romantic Symphony"), OPULENT side
7, side 8

Dvořák, No. 8 in G Major, Op. 88,
SLAVIC CONCERTS side 1 band 2,
side 2

Haydn, No. 48 in C Major ("Maria
Theresia"), ELEGANCE CONCERTS
side 1 band 2

SYMPHONIES: *Continued*

Haydn, No. 94 in G Major ("Surprise"), ELEGANCE side 1 band 2

Hindemith, *Mathis der Maler* Symphony, TODAY CONCERTS side 5

Lalo, *Symphonie espagnole,* Op. 21, SPANISH CONCERTS side 4, side 5 band 1

Mahler, No. 2 in C Minor ("Resurrection"), PRELUDE CONCERTS side 4, side 5, side 6, side 7

Mahler, No. 4 in G Major, PRELUDE side 3, side 4

Mendelssohn, No. 3 in A Minor, Op. 56 ("Scotch"), ROMANTIC CONCERTS side 1 band 2, side 2

Mozart, No. 39 in E Flat Major, K. 543, ELEGANCE CONCERTS side 10

Prokofiev, *Classical Symphony,* Op. 25 (No. 1 in D Major), TWENTIETH side 5 band 1

Prokofiev, No. 5 in B Flat Major, Op. 100, TWENTIETH CONCERTS side 9 band 3, side 10

Schubert, No. 5 in B Flat Major, D. 485, REVOLUTION side 2

Schubert, No. 9 in C Major ("The Great"), D. 944, REVOLUTION CONCERTS side 9, side 10

Shostakovich, No. 9, Op. 70, TODAY CONCERTS side 8

Stravinsky, in Three Movements, TWENTIETH CONCERTS side 6

Tchaikovsky, No. 5 in E Minor, Op. 64, OPULENT CONCERTS side 9, side 10

Vaughan Williams, No. 6 in E Minor, TODAY side 2, side 3 band 1

T

Tale of Czar Saltan, The: Suite, Op. 57, Rimsky-Korsakov, SLAVIC side 7 band 2

"Tales from the Vienna Woods" Waltz, Op. 325, Strauss II, OPULENT CONCERTS side 5 band 1

Tales of Hoffman, The: Act 2, Offenbach, OPULENT CONCERTS side 4

TALLIS, Thomas:

"Ecce tempus idoneum," RENAISSANCE side 6 band 1

"Gloria tibi Trinitas," RENAISSANCE CONCERTS side 1 band 2

"Jesu Salvator saeculi," RENAISSANCE side 6 band 2

"Spem in Alium," RENAISSANCE CONCERTS side 1 band 1

TCHAIKOVSKY, Peter Ilich:

Romeo and Juliet Fantasy Overture, OPULENT side 3 band 2

Swan Lake, Op. 20: Suite, OPULENT side 6

Symphony No. 5 in E Minor, Op. 64, OPULENT CONCERTS side 9, side 10

TELEMANN, Georg Philipp:

Concerto in B Flat Major for Three Oboes, Three Violins and Basso Continuo, BAROQUE side 2 band 1

Suite in C Major ("Water Music"), BAROQUE CONCERTS side 1

Tempranica, La: "Zapateado," Giménez, SPANISH CONCERTS side 8 band 1

Theater Music and Songs, Purcell. *See* THE BAROQUE ERA side 1

THEILE, Johann, "Was acht' ich deine Gunst?", RENAISSANCE CONCERTS side 8 band 6

"This Sweet and Merry Month," Byrd, RENAISSANCE side 2 band 5

Three-Cornered Hat, The, Falla, SPANISH side 7 band 3, side 8

Till Eulenspiegel, Richard Strauss, PRELUDE side 1 band 1

"Timor et tremor," Giovanni Gabrieli, RENAISSANCE CONCERTS side 3 band 3

Toccata and Fugue in D Minor, BWV. 565, Bach, BAROQUE side 6 band 3

TODAY, THE MUSIC OF

Side 1

Band 1, Shostakovich, *Festival*

Overture, Op. 96

Band 2, Walton, Suite from *Henry V:* Overture ("The Globe Playhouse"), Passacaglia ("Death of Falstaff"), "Charge and Battle," "Touch her soft lips and part," "Agincourt Song"

Side 2, Vaughan Williams, Symphony No. 6 in E Minor: Beginning

Side 3

Band 1, Vaughan Williams, Symphony No. 6 in E Minor: Conclusion

Band 2, Hindemith, Concerto for Horn and Orchestra

Side 4

Band 1, Boulez, *Le Soleil des Eaux*

Band 2, Britten, "Four Sea Interludes," Op. 33A (from *Peter Grimes)*

Side 5, Copland, *Appalachian Spring*

Side 6

Band 1, Babbitt, Ensembles for Synthesizer, Part 1

Band 2, Bernstein, *Fancy Free:* "Opening Dance," "Scene at the Bar," "Pas de Deux," "Variations," Finale

Side 7, Shostakovich, *The Execution of Stepan Razin,* Op. 119

Side 8, Poulenc, Concerto in G Minor for Organ, Strings and Timpani

TODAY, THE MUSIC OF (CONCERTS)
Side 1
 Bands 1-3, Walton, Partita for Orchestra
 Band 4, Walton, *Belshazzar's Feast:* Beginning
Side 2, Walton, *Belshazzar's Feast:* Conclusion
Side 3
 Band 1, Vaughan Williams, "The Lark Ascending," A Romance for Violin and Orchestra
 Band 2, Copland, *Rodeo:* "Buckaroo Holiday"
 Band 3, Copland, *Rodeo:* "Corral Nocturne"
Side 4
 Band 1, Copland, *Rodeo:* "Saturday Night Waltz"
 Band 2, Copland, *Rodeo:* "Hoe-Down"
 Band 3, Bernstein, *Facsimile*
Side 5, Hindemith, *Mathis der Maler* Symphony
Side 6, Britten, *Variations on a Theme of Frank Bridge,* Op. 10
Side 7, Poulenc, *Concert champêtre*
Side 8, Shostakovich, Symphony No. 9, Op. 70
Side 9, Vaughan Williams, *Hodie* (A Christmas Cantata): Beginning (I. Prologue: "Nowell! Nowell!", II. Narration: "Now the birth of Jesus Christ," III. Song: "It was the Winter wilde," IV. Narration: "And it came to pass in those days," V. Choral: "The blessed Son of God," VI. Narration: "And there were in the same country," VII. Song ("The Oxen"): "Christmas Eve and twelve of the clock," VIII. Narration: "And the shepherds returned")
Side 10, Vaughan Williams, *Hodie:* Conclusion (IX. Pastoral: "The shepherds sing," X. Narration: "But Mary kept all these things," XI. Lullaby: "Sweet was the song the Virgin sang," XII. Hymn: "Bright portals of the sky," XIII. Narration: "Now when Jesus was born," XIV: The March of the Three Kings: "From kingdoms of wisdom," XV. Choral: "No sad thought his soul affright," XVI. Epilogue: "In the beginning was the Word")

TOMKINS, Thomas, "Worcester Brawls," RENAISSANCE CONCERTS side 6 band 8

Tonadillas al estilo antiguo, Granados, SPANISH side 3 band 5

TORREJON Y VELASCO, Tomás de, *La Púrpura de la rosa:* Nymphs' Chorus and Loa, SPANISH CONCERTS side 3 band 5

Traviata, La: Selections, Verdi, ROMANTIC side 3 band 4

Trio in B Flat Major, Op. 97 ("Archduke"), Beethoven, REVOLUTION CONCERTS side 7 band 4, side 8

"Triana," Albéniz, SPANISH side 2 band 2

Tristan und Isolde: Prelude and Liebestod, Wagner, OPULENT CONCERTS side 1 band 1

"Trout Quintet" (in A Major, Op. 114) for piano and strings, Schubert, REVOLUTION CONCERTS side 3, side 4 band 1

Trovatore, Il: Selections, Verdi, ROMANTIC side 3 band 1

Troyens, Les: Royal Hunt and Storm, Berlioz, ROMANTIC CONCERTS side 6 band 2

Tudor England, Songs and Dances of. *See* FROM THE RENAISSANCE CONCERTS side 6

TURINA, Joaquín:
  Danzas Fantásticas, SPANISH side 1 band 2
  La Oración del torero, SPANISH CONCERTS side 7 band 2
  Rapsodia sinfonica, SPANISH CONCERTS side 7 band 3

TWENTIETH CENTURY, THE EARLY
  Side 1, Schoenberg, *Verklärte Nacht,* Op. 4
  Side 2

  Band 1, Berg, Four Pieces for Clarinet and Piano, Op. 5
  Band 2, Stravinsky, *Le Sacre du Printemps,* Part 1: "L'Adoration de la terre"
Side 3
  Band 1, Stravinsky, *Le Sacre du Printemps,* Part 2: "Le Sacrifice"
  Band 2, Bartók, Concerto for Orchestra: Beginning
Side 4, Bartók, Concerto for Orchestra: Conclusion
Side 5
  Band 1, Prokofiev, *Classical Symphony,* Op. 25
  Band 2, Stravinsky, Concerto in D Major for String Orchestra
Side 6
  Band 1, Schoenberg, Piano Pieces *(Klavierstücke),* Op. 33A and 33B
  Band 2, Webern, Three Songs, Op. 23: "Das dunkle Herz," "Es stürzt aus Höhen Frische," "Herr Jesus mein"
  Band 3, Milhaud, *La Création du monde*
Side 7
  Band 1, Gershwin, *An American in Paris*
  Band 2, Villa-Lobos, *Bachianas Brasileiras* No. 5: Aria *(Cantilena),* Dansa *(Martelo)*

Side 8, Prokofiev, Concerto No. 3 in C Major, Op. 26 for piano

TWENTIETH CENTURY, THE EARLY (CONCERTS)

Side 1, Stravinsky, *Pulcinella:* Suite

Side 2, Bartók, Concerto No. 3 for Piano and Orchestra

Side 3

    Band 1, Villa-Lobos, *Bachianas Brasileiras* No. 1: Introduction *(Embolada)*

    Band 2, Villa-Lobos, *Bachianas Brasileiras* No. 1: Prelude *(Modinha)*

    Band 3, Villa-Lobos, *Bachianas Brasileiras* No. 1: Fugue *(Conversa)*

    Band 4, Gershwin, *"I Got Rhythm" Variations*

Side 4

    Band 1, Webern, Five Pieces for Orchestra, Op. 10: "Sehr ruhig und zart," "Lebhaft und zart bewegt," "Sehr langsam und äusserst ruhig," "Fliessend, äusserst zart," "Sehr fliessend"

    Band 2, Berg, *Lulu:* Act 1, Scene 3

    Band 3, Berg, *Lulu:* Act 3

Side 5

    Band 1, Milhaud, *Suite française:* "Normandie," "Ile-de-France," "Alsace-Lorraine," "Provence"

    Band 2, Schoenberg, Six Pieces for Male Chorus, Op. 35: "Hemmung," "Das Gesetz," "Ausdrucksweise," "Glück," "Landsknechte," "Verbundenheit"

Side 6, Stravinsky, Symphony in Three Movements

Side 7, Bartók, Music for String Instruments, Percussion and Celesta

Side 8, Prokofiev, *Alexander Nevsky* Cantata, Op. 78: Beginning

    Band 1, "Russia under the Mongolian Yoke"

    Band 2, "Song about Alexander Nevsky"

    Band 3, "The Crusaders in Pskov"

    Band 4, "Arise, Ye Russian People"

    Band 5, "The Battle on the Ice"

Side 9

    Band 1, Prokofiev, *Alexander Nevsky* Cantata, Op. 78: "The Field of the Dead"

    Band 2, Prokofiev, *Alexander Nevsky* Cantata, Op. 78: "Alexander's Entry into Pskov"

    Band 3, Prokofiev, Symphony No. 5 in B Flat Major, Op. 100: Beginning

Side 10, Prokofiev, Symphony No. 5 in B Flat Major, Op. 100: Conclusion

V

VALDERRABANO, Enriquez de, "¿De dónde venís, amore?", SPANISH side 3 band 3

Valse, La, Ravel, PRELUDE CONCERTS side 2 band 2

Variations on a Theme of Frank Bridge, Op. 10, Britten, TODAY CONCERTS side 6

VAUGHAN WILLIAMS, Ralph:
  Hodie, TODAY CONCERTS side 9, side 10
  "The Lark Ascending," TODAY CONCERTS side 3 band 1
  Symphony No. 6 in E Minor, TODAY side 2, side 3 band 1

Venice, Ceremonial Music of, by Andrea and Giovanni Gabrieli. *See* FROM THE RENAISSANCE side 1

"Vere languores," Victoria, SPANISH side 7 band 1

VERDI, Guiseppe:
  Un Ballo in Maschera: Selections, ROMANTIC side 3 band 3
  Macbeth: Selections, ROMANTIC side 3 band 2
  Requiem Mass: Excerpts, ROMANTIC CONCERTS side 9, side 10

La Traviata: Selections, ROMANTIC side 3 band 4

Il Trovatore: Selections, ROMANTIC side 3 band 1

Verklärte Nacht, Op. 4, Schoenberg, TWENTIETH side 1

Versailles, Marches and Ballet Music for. *See* FROM THE RENAISSANCE CONCERTS side 8

Vesperae Solemnes de Confessore, K. 339: "Laudate Dominum," Mozart, ELEGANCE CONCERTS side 2 band 4

VICTORIA, Tomás Luis de:
  "O Magnum Mysterium," SPANISH CONCERTS side 3 band 4
  "Vere languores," "Ave Maria," SPANISH side 7 band 1

Vida Breve, La: Act 2, Scene 1, Falla, SPANISH side 1 band 1

VILLA-LOBOS, Heitor:
  Bachianas Brasileiras No. 1, TWENTIETH CONCERTS side 3 band 1
  Bachianas Brasileiras No. 5, TWENTIETH side 7 band 2

"Villanelle," Berlioz, ROMANTIC CONCERTS side 3 band 5

VIOLIN MUSIC:
  Bach, Concerto in D Minor for Two Violins and Strings, BWV. 1043, BAROQUE CONCERTS side 5 band 1
  Beethoven, Sonata No. 5 in F Major, Op. 24 ("Spring") for violin and

61

VIOLIN MUSIC: *Continued*

    piano, ELEGANCE CONCERTS side 3

    Lalo, *Symphonie espagnole*, Op. 21, SPANISH CONCERTS side 4, side 5 band 1

    Mendelssohn, Concerto in E Minor, Op. 64, ROMANTIC side 4

    Saint-Saëns, Concerto No. 3 in B Minor, Op. 61, OPULENT CONCERTS side 7

    Saint-Saëns, Introduction and Rondo Capriccioso, Op. 28, OPULENT side 5 band 2

    Vaughan Williams, "The Lark Ascending," TODAY CONCERTS side 3 band 1

VIVALDI, Antonio:

    Concerto in A Major for Two Orchestras, BAROQUE CONCERTS side 5 band 4

    Vivaldi-Bach, Concerto in A Minor for Four Harpsichords and Strings, BWV. 1065, BAROQUE side 2 band 2

    Concerto in D Major, Op. 10 No. 3 ("Il Gardellino") for flute, BAROQUE side 3 band 2

    Gloria, BAROQUE CONCERTS side 9 band 4, side 10

Vltava (The Moldau), Smetana, SLAVIC side 2 band 1

"Vos me matásteis," Rodrigo, SPANISH CONCERTS side 6 band 1

W

Wachet auf, ruft uns die Stimme (Sleepers Awake), Bach, BAROQUE CONCERTS side 2 band 3, side 3

WAGNER, Richard:

    Götterdämmerung: Siegfried's Funeral March, OPULENT CONCERTS side 1 band 2

    Lohengrin: Bridal Chamber Scene, OPULENT CONCERTS side 6

    Die Meistersinger von Nürnberg: Prelude, OPULENT side 1 band 1

    Tristan und Isolde: Prelude and Liebestod, OPULENT CONCERTS side 1 band 1

    Die Walküre: Act 3, Scene 3 (Conclusion), OPULENT side 4

"Waldesgespräch," Schumann, ROMANTIC side 6 band 4

Walküre, Die: Act 3, Scene 3, (Conclusion), Wagner, OPULENT side 4

WALTON, William:

    Belshazzar's Feast, TODAY CONCERTS side 1 band 4, side 2

    Henry V: Suite, TODAY side 1 band 2

    Partita for Orchestra, TODAY CONCERTS side 1 band 1

Waltz No. 6 in D-Flat Major, Op. 64 No.

1; No. 7 in C-Sharp Minor, Op. 64 No. 2; No. 8 in A-Flat Major, Op. 64 No. 3, Chopin, ROMANTIC side 2 band 4

"Was acht' ich deine Gunst?", Theile, RENAISSANCE CONCERTS side 8 band 6

Water Music (Suite in G Major, Suite in D Major), Handel, BAROQUE side 8

Water Music (Suite in C Major), Telemann, BAROQUE CONCERTS side 1

"Watkin's Ale," Anon., RENAISSANCE side 2 band 7

WEBER, Karl Maria von:

  Der Freischütz: Overture, REVOLUTION side 1 band 2

  Invitation to the Dance, Op. 65, REVOLUTION CONCERTS side 4 band 3

  Oberon: Selections, REVOLUTION CONCERTS side 6

WEBERN, Anton:

  Five Pieces for Orchestra, Op. 10, TWENTIETH CONCERTS side 4 band 1

  Three Songs, Op. 23, TWENTIETH side 6 band 2

WEELKES, Thomas, "Sing we at pleasure,"
RENAISSANCE side 2 band 1

"Where griping grief," Edwards, RENAISSANCE CONCERTS side 6 band 6

WILBYE, John:

  "Adieu, sweet Amaryllis," RENAISSANCE side 2 band 8

  "Draw on, sweet night," RENAISSANCE CONCERTS side 6 band 5

William Tell: Ballet Music, Rossini, REVOLUTION CONCERTS side 5 band 2

Wind Sextet *(Mládí),* Janáček, SLAVIC CONCERTS side 4 band 1

"Worcester Brawls," Tomkins, RENAISSANCE CONCERTS side 6 band 8

Z

"Zapateado," Giménez, SPANISH CONCERTS side 8 band 1

Zarzuela Arias. *See* THE SPANISH STYLE side 6; THE SPANISH STYLE CONCERTS side 8

"Zefiro torna," Monteverdi, RENAISSANCE CONCERTS side 2 band 1

ACKNOWLEDGMENTS

In connection with the recordings used in *The Story of Great Music* and *Concerts of Great Music,* the editors of TIME-LIFE RECORDS wish to acknowledge their indebtedness to Patti Laursen (repertory and discographic assistance) and to Carson Taylor (edit engineering), both of Capitol Records, Inc.

PRODUCTION MANAGER: LOUIS BRONZO
DESIGNER: MILDRED COIRO GALLO
ART CONSULTANT: EARLE G. KERSH

A CALENDAR

1825	1850	1875	1900	1925	1950

Johann Strauss II 1825-1899

Borodin 1833-1887

Brahms 1833-1897

Saint-Saëns 1835-1921

Balakirev 1837-1910

Bizet 1838-1875

Moussorgsky 1839-1881

Tchaikovsky 1840-1893

Chabrier 1841-1894

Dvořák 1841-1904

Rimsky-Korsakov 1844-1908

Janáček 1854-1928

Puccini 1858-1924

Albéniz 1860-1909

Mahler 1860-1911

Debussy 1862-1918

Richard Strauss 1864-1949

Vaughan Williams 1872-1958

Rachmaninoff 1873-1943

Schoenberg 1874-1951

Ravel 1875-1937

Falla 1876-1946